*Women Opening the Word*

*Paul: by the Grace of God*

*Casandra Martin*

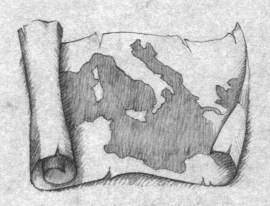

21ST CENTURY CHRISTIAN

ISBN: 0-89098-296-1
Copyright © 2004 by
21st Century Christian
2809 Granny White Pike
Nashville, Tennessee 37204
All rights reserved.
First Edition 1999, Third Edition 2004

Cover design by Caleb Gray.

# The Purpose

The purpose of these Bible lessons is to help you, through the life of Paul, stir your passion for Jesus, strengthen your commitment to His word, and deepen your resolve to walk daily by the grace of God. As we learn what it means to more fully give ourselves in service to Jesus, I pray that His name will be lifted up before men and His glory will shine in all the earth.

May God richly bless you as you study His word.

# How to Use This Study

This Bible study was written with you in mind. It contains some special features designed to help and guide you through your study of the life of the apostle Paul.

 Check the WORD! You will see this symbol when you are to refer to Scripture. You will need your Bible for each lesson. Choose an accurate, reliable, and readable translation. This study specifically refers to the New International Version (NIV). New King James, New American Standard, and New Revised Standard are also excellent translations. Please be careful about using The Message, Phillips, or The Living Bible. While readable, they are not accurate translations.

 Map out Paul's journeys. You will see this symbol when you are to refer to a map. By tracing Paul's travels on a map, it will help cement the movement of God's grace as it spreads through the world.

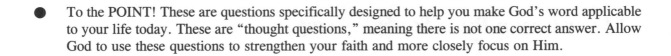 To the POINT! These are questions specifically designed to help you make God's word applicable to your life today. These are "thought questions," meaning there is not one correct answer. Allow God to use these questions to strengthen your faith and more closely focus on Him.

 Indicates a message from the heart. Follow carefully these inspirational thoughts which have one purpose in mind: to make God's love more real to you than ever before.

Day 1 – Day 4    Each lesson is broken into four parts. Each week as you sit down to do your lesson begin with Day 1. The next day work on Day 2, and so forth. This way you will be able to complete each week's lesson comfortably. Spreading your work on each week's lesson over the four days will allow you to be in God's word on a regular basis as well as help you glean God's blessings and life lessons for your heart today.

# Study Group Formats

There are as many different ways to effectively use this study as there are people excited about learning God's word. Below are three suggestions for group and/or individual study. Feel free to adapt the format to meet your group or individual study needs.

## 45-minute Bible Class Format

This book is an excellent tool for a Bible class study. I would recommend using the book in this setting in the following way:

1. Pray each time you begin that God's Spirit will guide you as you study and open your eyes to His word.

2. Divide each lesson into two parts. Using the Day 1-4 markers, ask your class to study Days 1 and 2 on week one, Days 3 and 4 on week two, and so forth. There is enough material in each two-day block to meet the needs of your class time.

3. Each member of the class should be encouraged to do the lesson before the weekly class time. Your job as teacher is not to go through the material question by question but rather to organize the discussion around the central theme of that week's lesson. Choose several of the " ● To the POINT! " questions that you find to be most relevant and make those the foundation of your discussion. These questions are designed to stimulate discussion and focus the class on the personal application of the lesson. Encourage the class members to share their impressions, questions, new insights, and challenges on a weekly basis.

4. Enjoy the richness of God's word.

## 1½ – 2 hour Group Bible Study Format

This book is an excellent tool for a group Bible study. I would recommend using the book in this setting in the following way:

1. Pray each time you begin that God's Spirit will guide you as you study and open your eyes to His word.

2. Do one lesson a week. There is enough material in each lesson block to meet the needs of your group study time.

3. Divide your Bible study group into small discussion groups of 6-12 individuals. These small groups allow more active participation, enhance fellowship and a sense of belonging, and permit friendship and intimacy to grow as the groups share personal reflections of the Bible study and prayer.

4.  Each small group should have a leader and an assistant leader. The responsibilities of the group leader are:

    · prepare for and lead the weekly discussion of the small group
    · encourage participation of all members of the group during the discussion

    The responsibilities of the assistant leader are:

    · contact group members weekly to encourage involvement and participation
    · be available to lead the discussion if the group leader must be absent

5.  Each member of the group should be encouraged to do the lesson before the weekly class time. Your job as group leader is not to go through the material question by question but rather to organize the discussion around the central theme of that week's lesson. Choose several of the " ● To the POINT! " questions that you find to be most relevant and make those the foundation of your discussion. These questions are designed to stimulate discussion and focus the class on the personal application of the lesson. Encourage the group members to share their impressions, questions, new insights, and challenges on a weekly basis.

6.  Another helpful tool is to have a group leader's meeting for approximately 30 minutes prior to the beginning of class. This gives the group leaders an opportunity to share their insights, answer questions, and make sure that everyone understands the central focus of the week's study.

7.  Enjoy the richness of God's word.

## *Individual Study*

This book is an excellent tool for a personal Bible study. I would recommend using the book in this setting in the following way:

1.  Pray each time you begin that God's Spirit will guide you as you study and open your eyes to His word.

2.  Each lesson is broken into four parts. Each week as you sit down to do your lesson, begin with Day 1. The next day work on Day 2, and so forth. This way you will be able to complete each week's lesson comfortably. Spreading your work on each week's lesson over the four days will allow you to be in God's word on a regular basis as well as help you glean God's blessings and life lessons for your heart today.

3.  Enjoy the richness of God's word.

God bless you! You are about to take an exciting journey – into the grace of God!

# Contents

# Timeline

Adapted from Conybeare & Howson

| A.D. | Paul | Contemporary Events | A.D. | Paul | Contemporary Events |
|------|------|---------------------|------|------|---------------------|
| 30 | Establishment of Church in Jerusalem | | 55 | At Ephesus. | |
| 36 | Death of Stephen | | 56 | At Ephesus. | |
| | (?) Paul's conversion. | | 57 | (Spring) - writes *1 Cor.* (Summer) - Leaves Ephesus for Macedonia. (Autumn) - writes *2 Cor.* and then (Winter) - goes to Corinth. | |
| 37 | (?) At Damascus. | Death of Tiberius and accession of Caligula (March 16). | | | |
| 38 | (?) Flight from Damascus to Jerusalem, and then to Tarsus. | | | | |
| 39 | (?) During these years Paul preaches in Syria and Cilicia, making Tarsus his headquarters. | Death of Caligula and accession of Claudius (Jan. 25), Judea and Samaria given to Herod Agrippa I. | 58 | (Spring) - writes *Romans*, and leaves Corinth, going to Philippi and Miletus (Summer) - to Jerusalem (Pentecost), where he is arrested and sent to Cesarea. | |
| 40 | | | | | |
| 41 | | | | | |
| 43 | | | | | |
| 44 | Brought from Tarsus to Antioch (Acts 11:26), and stays there a year before the famine. | Death of Herod Agrippa I (Acts 12) Cuspius Fadus (as procurator) succeeds to the government of Judea. | 59 | At Cesarea. | Nero murders Agrippina. |
| | | | 60 | (Autumn) - Sent to Rome by Festus (about August). (Winter) - shipwrecked at Malta. | Felix is recalled and succeeded by Festus. |
| 45 | Visits Jerusalem with Barnabas to relieve the famine. | | 61 | (Spring) - Arrives in Rome. | |
| 46 | At Antioch. | Tiberius Alexander made procurator of Judea. | 62 | At Rome. (Spring) - writes *Philemon, Colossians, Ephesians.* (Autumn) - writes *Philippians.* | Burrus dies; Albinus succeeds Festus as Procurator; Nero marries Poppea; Octavia executed; Pallas put to death. |
| 47 | At Antioch. | | | | |
| 48 | **'First Missionary Journey'** from Antioch to Cyprus, Antioch in Pisidian, Iconium, Lystra, Derbe, and back through the same places to Antioch. | Agrippa II (Acts 25) made king of Chalcis; Cumanus made procurator of Judea. | 63 | (Spring) - He is acquitted and goes to Macedonia (Phil 2:24) and to Asia Minor (Philemon 22). | Poppea's daughter Claudia is born. |
| 49 | | | | | |
| | | | 64 | (?) Goes to Spain. | Great fire at Rome (July 19), followed by persucution of Roman Christians. |
| 50 | Paul and Barnabas attend the 'Council of Jerusalem' — writes *Galatians* | | | | |
| 51 | **'Second Missionary Journey'** from Antioch to Cilicia, Lycaonia, Galatia, Troas, Philippi, Thessalonica, Berea, Athens, and Corinth — writes *1 Thessalonians.* | Claudius expels the Jews from Rome (Acts 18:2). | 65 | (?) In Spain. | Gessius Florus made procurator of Judea. Conspiracy of Piso and death of Seneca. |
| 52 | | | | | |
| 53 | At Corinth — writes *2 Thessalonians.* | The tetrachy of Trachonitis given to Agrippa II; Felix made procurator of Judea. | 66 | (Summer) - From Spain (?) to Asia Minor (1 Tim. 1:3) | The Jewish war begins. |
| | | | 67 | (Summer) - writes *1 Tim.* from Macedonia. (Autumn) - writes *Titus* from Ephesus. (Winter) - At Troas. | |
| 54 | (Spring) Leaves Corinth and reaches... (Summer) Jerusalem at Pentecost and then goes to Antioch. (Autumn) **'Third Missionary Journey'** to Ephesus. | Death of Claudius and accession of Nero (Oct. 13). | 68 | (Spring) - In prison at Rome; writes *2 Tim.* (Summer) - Executed (May or June) | Death of Nero in the middle of June. |

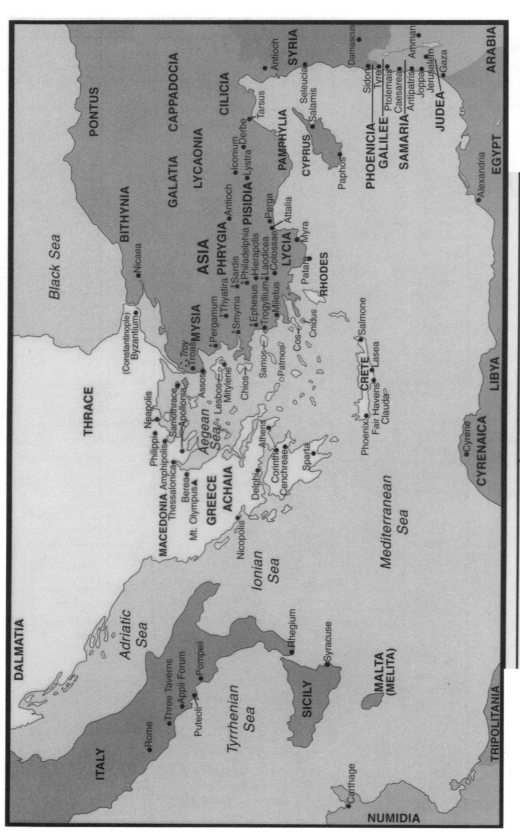

**Paul's First Journey**

One of the Seven Churches of Asia (Rev. 1-3)
• City or Town
∴ Ancient Ruins/Sites
▲ Mountain

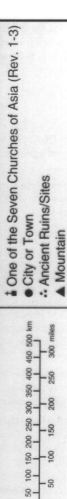

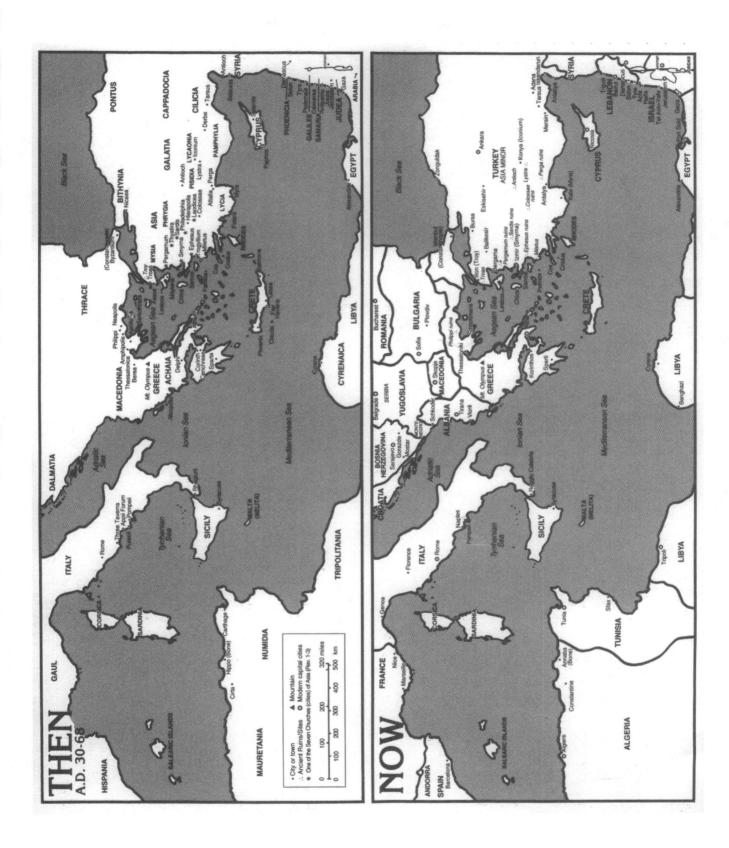

# Paul: By the Grace of God
# Introduction

*"By the grace of God I am what I am, and His grace to me was not without effect."*
— **Paul**, 1 Corinthians 15:10

The apostle Paul. The mention of his name brings to mind a giant of faith, a prolific writer, a man who almost single-handedly brought the gospel of Jesus to the entire Roman world.

Yet Paul would not have described himself in any of those terms. He saw himself as a flawed, sinful man rescued by the love and mercy of Jesus Christ. Everything done during his life he did for love of his Lord.

What is remarkable about Paul is his single-minded focus on Jesus Christ. There is not a moment that he does not have his eyes fixed on the Savior. Paul's passion for Jesus erupts in a bright flame that shines for the world to see.

As we walk with Paul and his companions for the next several weeks, Paul will challenge us to give ourselves more fully to Jesus; to bring our lives more in focus with God's will; to more powerfully express our love for the Savior to those around us; to grow and *"be conformed to the likeness of his Son..."* Romans 8:29

Let's look at two verses that will serve as the foundation of our study of the life of Paul.

Fill in the blanks:

Philippians 3:8 (NIV) *"What is more, I consider everything a _____ compared to the _____ _____ of knowing _____ _____ my _____..."*

Paul will challenge you to make that statement your own.

Philippians 4:9 (NIV) *"Whatever you have _____ or _____ or _____ from me, or _____ in me — put it into _____."*

Can you say that to someone about your Christian walk?

Exciting days lay ahead. God is poised to do great things in you and through you. Your commitment to studying His word gives Him pleasure and honor. Be prepared to meet Him in unexpected ways and places. Through Paul, God will challenge us, love us, prod us, fill us with joy, cover our hearts in peace, light a fire in our souls, and bless us with a deeper understanding of Jesus.

1

# Grace:
# A New Beginning

I'm glad you have decided to study the life of Paul. Are you excited? I am. It's going to be a thrilling journey. Begin today by praying that God will open your heart to His word.

## DAY 1

The study of the life of Paul is uniquely tied to the New Testament book of Acts. Acts, written by Luke, is the only inspired record we have of the beginnings of the church. It ties the historical record of Jesus' ministry to the epistles that guide our daily Christian walk. Our study of the life of Paul must begin with the religious revolution that took place in Jerusalem as described in the first chapters of Acts. It is important to study these first days of the church so that we can see how and why Paul was God's choice to take this revolution to the world. The book of Acts begins ten days before the Jewish festival of Pentecost in the year 30 AD. Almost six weeks earlier at the Feast of Passover, Jesus was betrayed by one of His own, arrested, illegally tried, crucified on a Roman cross, buried, and resurrected by God on the third day. He has spent the last forty days with His disciples preparing them to spread the good news of salvation. The disciples have been on a roller coaster of emotion — fear, panic, denial, sorrow, horror, grief, desolation, and joy. As they stand on the Mount of Olives with Jesus, they are unaware of the enormity of the task that lies before them.

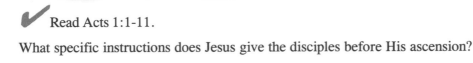 Read Acts 1:1-11.

What specific instructions does Jesus give the disciples before His ascension?

_____

_____

The disciples are told to return to Jerusalem to await a very special gift — the Holy Spirit.

● Who is the Holy Spirit? II Corinthians 13:14; John 15:26

_____

The Holy Spirit will give the apostles the power to carry their witness to all the peoples of the earth. The specific power promised to the apostles will bring with it the ability to do all kinds of miracles. The purpose of this power is to confirm the new message being proclaimed by those who are witnesses to the resurrection.

Jesus also gives the disciples a specific plan for taking the good news of salvation to the world. Read Acts 1:8. What is Jesus' four-step plan for the spread of the gospel?

_____

_____

This command to take the name of Jesus to the world is not just for first century apostles. It is also a personal, direct command to you, His witness in the world today. Jesus' four-step plan is still the most effective method for spreading the gospel in our own sphere of influence.

● In what way are you a witness for Jesus today? Do you feel a personal responsibility for taking the gospel to the world? Explain.

_____

_____

Our testimony to the power of Jesus begins in "Jerusalem," our own homes. This is where we have our most powerful and consistent influence. It is impossible to take the gospel elsewhere until we have made it the center of our own lives. The circle of our testimony then expands to "Judea," our friends and neighbors. These are the people who should daily see us walking in the light of Jesus. We are then told to go outside our comfort zone and take the message to "Samaria," speaking to those to whom we might not ordinarily talk, but who need the gentle touch of Jesus. Finally, we are compelled to go to "the ends of the earth," to spread the love of Jesus to everyone with whom we have contact.[1]

● How can the four-step plan be applied in your life today as you live as an example for Jesus?

_____

_____

Jesus returns to His Father's side in a cloud of glory as the disciples watch in amazement. His work of salvation is done and the apostles' job of spreading that salvation throughout the world is about to begin.

● Why does Jesus leave the job of spreading the gospel in our hands? II Corinthians 4:7

_____

_____

 *Locate Jerusalem on the map in the front of your book.*

Ten days pass as the apostles return to Jerusalem to await the promised Holy Spirit. It must have been difficult to be told to wait, but God is teaching them a valuable lesson — I am in control. Wait on my timing.

● When have you been told to wait on God? What lessons did you learn?

_____

_____

● Read Acts 1:14. How do the apostles spend these ten days? Why is this a good model for us when we are called to wait?

_____

_____

> ♥ Prayer focuses our minds on God, prepares our hearts for His will, and acknowledges our dependence on Him.

✔ Read Acts 2:1-13.

How does the Holy Spirit come upon the apostles on Pentecost?

_____

_____

On Sunday morning, the apostles are gathered together in prayer. Without warning, the sound of a violent wind, like a tornado, fills the room. Then what appear to be tongues of fire separate and come to rest on each apostle. This marks the filling of the apostles with the Holy Spirit as promised by Jesus.

● Why would God use wind and fire as symbols of the Spirit's coming? John 3:8; I Thessalonians 5:19

_____

_____

What is the immediate result of the apostles being filled with the Holy Spirit? How many different nationalities hear the wonders of God being told in their own tongues?

_____

What are the two different reactions of the people?

_____

God prepares the apostles to proclaim the crucified and risen Savior. With rushing wind and tongues of fire, the men who walked with Jesus are empowered to proclaim His name to men of every nation. By causing the apostles to speak in this way to the multitude, God is announcing that the message of salvation in Jesus is available to all people. The gift of grace will meet the deepest need of men's hearts and they will hear the good news in their own language.

# DAY 2

It is Sunday morning and as the Feast of Pentecost is being celebrated throughout Jerusalem, the Holy Spirit comes upon the apostles in a dramatic and powerful way. Peter now stands up to address the crowd. In perhaps the greatest sermon that has ever been preached, Peter, who had lied about even knowing Jesus seven weeks before, boldly stands up and proclaims His name to the crowd.

✔ Read Acts 2:14-41. Please read slowly and carefully. Our understanding of this material is absolutely fundamental to understanding the work of Jesus to save us, how we receive that salvation, and the primary purpose of the church in this world.

● What are the five important points Peter makes in his Pentecost sermon?

1 _____

2 _____

3 _____

4 _____

5 _____

As Peter speaks to the crowd, he makes five declarations about Jesus. These are the foundation of the Christian faith.

**First, Peter reminds the people of the many miracles that Jesus performed during His ministry.** These, he tells them, are proof that Jesus was sent from God.

● Which of Jesus' miracles most impresses you? Why?

_____

_____

Read John 10:22-25 and John 14:11. What decision does the ministry of Jesus demand?

_____

_____

**Second, Peter explains that Jesus' death and resurrection are the fulfillment of God's eternal plan.** These things were planned by God before creation. They speak to God's great love for us and His determination to reclaim His children from sin. God revealed His plan for man's redemption throughout the centuries through Old Testament prophecy. He wants us to know that His love for us is no accident or afterthought.

● Why is it important to understand the eternal nature of God's plan of salvation?
  Ephesians 1:4; Revelation 13:8

_____

_____


The creation of Adam and Eve, of people to fill the earth, was the work of God's heart. His love for man not only included giving him the breath of life, but the path of redemption. God, the Holy Three-in-One, prepared His answer for sin before Adam ever asked his first question. Before the first couple ever looked in wonder at the beauty of the garden, Jesus had looked at the agony of the cross. Our sin did not catch God by surprise. Before He made us, He knew our darkest secrets. And yet, He made us anyway. He chose to love you, to create you, to save you from before the beginning of time.

**Third, Peter places the responsibility for the death of Jesus squarely on the people listening.** The guilt for His death does not belong to the Jewish leaders' alone. The burden rests on the hearts of each individual who rejected Him.

Fill in the blank:

Acts 2:23 (NIV) *"This man was handed over to _____ by God's set purpose and*

*foreknowledge; and _____, with the help of wicked men, put him _____*

*_____ by _____ him to the _____."*


The Jews are not the only ones who bear responsibility for the death of Jesus. What responsibility do you bear for the death of Jesus? II Corinthians 5:21

_____


**Fourth, Peter testifies that Jesus has risen from the dead and that he, and the other apostles, are witnesses to this fact.**

The resurrection of Jesus is the single most important truth of the gospel.

● In what way is the resurrection the hinge point of Christianity? I Corinthians 15:12-20

_____

_____

**Fifth, at the end of his sermon, Peter tells the people that they can be certain that Jesus is both Lord and Christ.**

● How has the fact that Jesus is Lord and Christ made a difference in your life?

_____

_____

"Lord" is an ancient and revered name for God in the Old Testament. By naming Jesus as Lord, Peter ascribes Jesus as worthy of honor and obedience. In naming Jesus as Christ, Peter tells the people that He is the Messiah, the One promised to bring salvation to the world.

● What is your reaction to these truths?

_____

_____

What is reaction of the people? Acts 2:37

_____

Let us be very clear. The people in verse 37 are cut to the heart because they now believe that Jesus is the Christ, the Son of God. Yet, belief alone is not enough for salvation. They understand that belief in Jesus now requires action.

What does Peter tell the people to do? Write Acts 2:38.

_____

_____

_____

Go back and underline what Peter tells us to do to receive forgiveness. Put a box around who is to follow this command. Circle what you will receive through the name of Jesus.

Salvation is an active, not passive, process. God acts on our behalf through Jesus. He came to this earth, lived, died, and rose again. He expects us to act in obedience to receive His precious gift of grace — to repent, be baptized, and thus be saved. This is not the creed of a man-made religious group. Baptism is the express command of God Himself. There are no exceptions — this is the plan of salvation laid out by God through Jesus.

Have you repented and been baptized for the forgiveness of your sins according to God's command?

_____

● What is the promise that accompanies repentance and baptism?

_____

This is a very special gift. While different from the extraordinary power the apostles received, the presence of the Holy Spirit is precious in the heart of the believer.

● What assurances come from the Spirit dwelling within us?

Romans 8:26-27 _____

II Corinthians 1:21-22 _____

Galatians 5:22-23 _____

Ephesians 1:13-14 _____

II Thessalonians 2:13 _____

John 14:16 _____

For whom is the command and the promise in Acts 2:39 according to Peter?

_____

Peter probably never dreamed that he would be talking to you and me 2000 years later! As Peter speaks, God lays bare the gulf created by our sin and the full extent of His love for each of us. The cross becomes the remedy to man's deepest need. The blood of Jesus is the bridge that allows us to enter into the presence of God. He has paid the price. He extends His nail-scarred hand. The choice is yours.

# DAY 3

The church of Jesus has started in a powerful way on Pentecost Sunday. The apostles have been given an extraordinary filling of the Holy Spirit and 3,000 believers are baptized and become the core of the new church. Today we are going to take notice of some important characteristics of these early Christians and look at the unique way they join together in these first years of Christianity.

✔ Read Acts 2:42-47 and Acts 4:32-37.

To what four things do the new Christians devote themselves?

_____

_____

● Define devotion.

_____

● To what do you devote yourself in your Christian walk?

_____

_____

Devotion involves more than taking a passing interest in something. It means they sacrificed time for other interests so they could do these four things. Anytime we read of godly people being devoted to something, we should take notice. These four things – devoting themselves to the apostles' teaching, fellowship, breaking of bread, and prayer — are the very things which we as Christians today must commit ourselves. Their example is our pattern.

The first thing to which they are devoted is Bible study!! Of course, they do not have the written Scriptures that we have, rather they listen and learn directly from the men who walked with Jesus.

● Why is study of God's word the first thing to which we should be devoted?

_____

_____

God's word is the catalyst for all spiritual growth. These new Christians hungered to grow. The world offers many "fast-food" alternatives to take the edge off our hunger for God, but only by digging deeply into God's word will we satisfy the soul that *"hungers and thirsts for righteousness."*
Matthew 5:6

The second thing to which the new church is devoted is fellowship. A heart that loves Jesus longs to be with those who are like-minded. This type of fellowship involves more than simply socializing. It is a deeply spiritual time during which these Christians discuss their walk with Jesus.

● Why is fellowship important to your Christian walk?

_____

_____

The breaking of bread speaks of their attention to the weekly participation in the Lord's Supper as taught by the apostles.

● Why does Jesus command us to remember Him in this way?

_____

_____

The purpose of the Lord's Supper is two-fold. It is first a memorial which focuses our hearts on Jesus Christ, our crucified and risen Savior. Our hearts are so easily turned by other concerns. The Lord knows we need this weekly reminder that He is to be the center of our hearts. This time should be the most important time in our worship together. Second, the Lord's Supper is a testimony of our faith in the resurrection of Jesus. By participating in the Lord's Supper, we announce to the world our belief in the power of God.

● These early Christians are devoted to prayer. Why is prayer so important in a believer's life?

_____

_____

Prayer is our vital link to the Father. Going daily into God's presence refreshes us, humbles us, empowers us, and deepens our friendship with our Lord. How often do you talk to your best friend? Now consider devoting that much time to prayer and watch what happens to your relationship with God!!

Stop and look back at these four areas of the Christian life. To which of these do you need to more fully devote yourself? How do you plan to do that this week?

_____

_____

● Read Acts 2:42-47 and Acts 4:32-37. What standard of generosity do the first century Christians give us? Why are they able to give so generously? How does our society make this attitude of generosity difficult?

_____

_____

_____

Generosity! These passages have often been misunderstood as some sort of communal living arrangement, but that is not the case at all. There is a unique situation in Jerusalem at this time. Go back to Acts 2:8-11. Jews from at least fifteen different countries have gathered together in Jerusalem for Pentecost. Many of these are the first Christians. They continue on in Jerusalem for a period of time after the feast and now require assistance from the brothers in that area. Likewise, wealthy travelers are being generous to the poor of Jerusalem. Those that have plenty are giving to those who are in need.

What result does the unity of the new Christians have in the community in which they live?

_____

People are drawn to Christ by the changed lives of His followers. The way we live is a most powerful testimony to those around us.

Read Acts 5:11. What term is used to describe the group of believers at Jerusalem?

_____

This is the first time that the term "church" is used in reference to the followers of Jesus. The word in the original language is *ekklesia* and means "called out."

● Why is "called out" a good name for the body of Christ?

_____

_____

# DAY 4

We have watched as the new church of Jesus Christ has grown and reached out to offer the message of salvation to the people of Jerusalem. Thousands have been baptized. We have seen the transforming work of the Holy Spirit in the lives of the believers. Now we must back up and pick up another thread that has been running parallel to our story of the beginnings of God's church. It is time to bring out the baby pictures and meet a young Jewish man named Saul. While the details are sketchy, let's piece together a family portrait of the man we will come to know so well.

 Read Philippians 3:4-6 and Acts 22:2-3.

Where is Saul born? What nationality is Saul? Of what tribe?

_____

_____

Who is Saul's teacher? In regard to the Jewish religion, to which sect does he belong?

_____

_____

Saul is born in the early years of the first decade of the first century. Although the exact year is not known, estimates place his birth between 6 BC and 4 AD. He is born to Jewish parents in Tarsus in Cilicia, a Roman city.

 *Locate Tarsus on the map in the front of your book.*

Cilicia borders the Mediterranean Sea in southeast Asia Minor. Today we know it as Turkey. Tarsus is Cilicia's major city, lying on the trade route between Syria and Asia Minor. It is surrounded by fertile plains, mountains, rivers, and the sea. In 67 BC, Tarsus came under the rule of Rome but retained its status as a free city.

Despite growing up in a Jewish home, the city in which Saul is raised is decidedly Greek in flavor. The early first century geographer Strabo wrote that Tarsus was a center of learning, the arts, and a respected center of education.

Read Genesis 17:9-13. What happened to Saul on his eighth day? What is the significance of circumcision?

_____

_____

A Jewish male entered into the covenant between God and Israel by circumcision. Every Israelite boy had been circumcised on his eighth day since the time of Abraham.

● How do we enter into the covenant between God and the new Israel — the church? Colossians 2:9-12

_____

Read Luke 1:59-60. Another important event happens at the circumcision ceremony for the young baby. What else does the baby receive on the eighth day?

_____

Not only was the infant boy circumcised into the covenant of God, but it was also the day on which the child received his name.

As a Roman citizen, Paul received three names. A forename, the *praenomen*; a family name, the *nomen gentile*; and an additional name, the *cognomen*. Of these three names we are only told one — Paulus, which in English appears as Paul. Paul is his Roman name. In addition to the legal Roman names, the boy also receives a Jewish name — Saul.

Within thirty days of Saul's birth, his father was required to take him to the Roman authorities and have him registered as a Roman citizen by birth. Having been born a Roman citizen indicates that Saul's father was also a Roman citizen. How Saul's family attained its citizenship is unknown, but probably one of Saul's forefathers rendered a great service to a Roman official and was granted citizenship as a reward.

The privileges of Roman citizenship were extensive. These privileges included: a fair public trial if accused of a crime, exemption from certain forms of tortuous punishment, and protection from summary execution. Saul's citizenship would prove to be a great advantage. God needed a man who could travel extensively throughout the Roman world and achieve access to audiences that would be closed to a noncitizen.

As proof of his citizenship, young Saul receives a *diptych*. The diptych was a small pair of clay tablets that folded together containing a certified copy of Roman birth registration. Thus wherever Saul travels, he can prove his Roman citizenship.

● What advantages does your citizenship give you? How are you using that for Jesus?

_____

_____

Despite his Roman citizenship in a town of Greek culture, young Saul lives a sheltered life in a strictly Jewish home. In Philippians 3:5, Saul describes himself as a *"Hebrew of Hebrews"* and in Acts 23:6, he tells the Jewish leaders that he is *"a Pharisee, the son of a Pharisee."* These two phrases give us an important insight into the childhood of young Saul. There were two major groups of people in the Jewish community – the Hebraic Jews and the Grecian or Hellenist Jews. The Hebraic Jews spoke Hebrew and observed a strict Jewish lifestyle. We would call them orthodox Jews today. The Hellenistic Jews spoke Greek, were more relaxed in their observance of the Jewish law, and adopted many Greek ways into their lifestyle. Growing up in a Greek-speaking city like Tarsus, it would be expected that Saul would be a Hellenist Jew. Saul, however, says he is a Hebrew. This means he grew up in a strictly orthodox home. He certainly grew up speaking Greek, but at home and in the synagogue they spoke Aramaic, the language of Judea.

The strictest sect of the Jewish religion was the Pharisees. While the Pharisees do not have a good reputation in our day and Jesus was quite critical of their practices, we must understand that they were not seen in this light in the early first century. At this time, Israel had descended into apathy about the worship of Jehovah and the Mosaic Law. The Pharisees sought to bring adherence to the law and the worship of God back into focus as the center of Jewish life. The Pharisees would be considered the "conservatives" of the Jewish political system.

Saul's father is very diligent to give his son a proper Jewish upbringing according to the law. An ancient Talmudic writer said, "What is commanded of a father towards his son? To circumcise him, to teach him the law, to teach him a trade."[2]

We have already seen that Saul's family circumcised him on the eighth day, but what about the other two commands?

Read Acts 18:2-3. What is Paul's trade?

_____

Tentmaking is the trade that Saul's father teaches him growing up in Tarsus. The area of Cilicia was known for its fertile plains and the flax that was grown there and woven into linen. The area was also famous for a fabric called cilicium. It is a coarse, dark cloth woven from goat hair that was used to give protection from the elements. This is the fabric that Saul learns to use to make tents. Cilicium cloth can still be purchased in that area of the world today.

● What is your trade? How are you using it for Jesus?

_____

_____

Saul's spiritual education also starts at a very young age. He is schooled at home and then perhaps at the Hebraic synagogue. He begins studying and memorizing the Scriptures by age five. As a child, he commits to his mind and heart Deuteronomy 6:4-9 and many of the Psalms. His mind overflows with the ancient stories of Abraham, Isaac, and Jacob. He learns of the birth of Benjamin and the other eleven sons of Israel. His heart bursts with the stories of Moses, Joshua, and Aaron as they approached the Promised Land. His imagination soars as he learns of the heroics of Saul, David, and Solomon. He ponders the ancient prophecies of Isaiah. He weeps with Jeremiah over the destruction of Jerusalem.

● What impact do you think this early teaching of the Scriptures has on Saul throughout his life?

_____

_____

● Why is it important to teach our children the stories of Scripture? How do we do this effectively?

_____

_____

Write Deuteronomy 6:6-7.

_____

_____

_____

The word "impress" in this verse brings to mind the picture of stamping words or pictures in fresh clay. As the clay dries, the words and pictures become permanent.

● In what way is a child's heart like fresh clay?

_____

I am convinced that we greatly underestimate our children's ability and potential for learning the things of God. Children have a natural hunger to learn and love their Creator and we need to impress His love in their hearts while the clay is fresh.

That Saul is bright and diligent in his studies is a delight and honor to his parents.

Read Galatians 1:14. How does Paul describe his achievements in studying the Scriptures?

_____

Probably around age thirteen, Saul is sent to finish his formal education in Jerusalem. He studies under the leading Pharisee rabbi of the time — Gamaliel. Here young Saul learns the complicated oral traditions of the law, how to argue the intricacies of interpretation, to observe the law with the greatest strictness. Gamaliel is an excellent teacher for Saul. Not only is he an expert in the law, but Gamaliel gives his students a liberal arts education and encourages his students to expand their knowledge of the Greek world as well.

After completing his formal education, Saul returns to Tarsus either to take up the family trade of tentmaking or to serve as a rabbi in the local synagogue. There is no evidence from the New Testament that Saul was in Judea at the time of Jesus' ministry.

● In what ways does Saul's unique childhood prepare him to be God's ambassador to the Gentile world?

_____

_____

_____

● In what ways has God prepared you to be His ambassador to the world? (Consider your childhood, family, neighborhood, job, and education.)

_____

_____

_____

---

1 McGee, *Acts, Chapters 1-14,* p19
2 Conybeare, p39

# Amazing Grace

Last week we witnessed the birth of Christ's church and the man God would use to spread His grace throughout the world. This week we will watch in wonder as that grace reaches out and transforms the heart of an enemy into an ardent servant of Jesus Christ.

## DAY 1

Today we look at a dark moment in the history of the church. Between the dark clouds of persecution, however, God shows us the radiance of victory in Christ. Pray for open eyes today to see His glory.

The word of God now focuses our attention on one devout follower of Jesus — Stephen.

Read the following Scriptures and note the portrait the Holy Spirit paints of this man of God.

| | | |
|---|---|---|
| Acts 6:3 | A man full of | _____ |
| Acts 6:5 | A man full of | _____ |
| Acts 6:8 | A man full of | _____ |
| Acts 6:8 | A man able to do great | _____ |
| Acts 6:15 | A man with the face of | _____ |
| Acts 7 | A man with great knowledge of | _____ |
| Acts 7:51-53 | A man not afraid to | _____ |
| Acts 7:60 | A man able to | _____ |

Quite a man, isn't he? A man full of grace, truth, power, courage, love, and forgiveness. Stephen is certainly a powerful witness for Jesus.

How would the Holy Spirit describe your life?

_____

_____

● How do you develop a Christian character like Stephen's?

_____

_____

Stephen is the kind of Christian that people notice. His life is a powerful testimony to the love of Jesus. It is impossible to live a life fully devoted to Jesus Christ and not radiate His love and Spirit to those around you. This will bring mixed reactions. Some will be drawn to the light of God's love; while others will react negatively, even violently, to a life marked by forgiveness and peace.

Read Acts 6:8-15.

What is Stephen doing in Jerusalem that brings such hatred from the Jews?

_____

_____

What is the outcome of these religious discussions?

_____

Before what group is Stephen brought to defend himself? What is Stephen's countenance like during his trial?

_____

Stephen is charged with blasphemy against Moses and the temple and brought before the Sanhedrin for judgment. Caiaphas, the high priest at the trial of Jesus, commands Stephen to give his defense of the charges. As the Sanhedrin convenes, Stephen's face takes on the appearance of an angel.

Read Exodus 34:29. Whose face became radiant in the presence of God?

_____

● What will you look like if you spend time alone with God? What do you need to do today to help you make time to be alone with God?

_____

_____

It is no coincidence that as Stephen is brought up on charges of blaspheming Moses, God makes his face radiant like Moses' was after he spoke with God. You see, Stephen has also been in the presence of God. As a Christian, the Holy Spirit dwells in his heart. His appearance should have gotten the attention of the Sanhedrin. Instead, it hardens their hearts further.

Stephen, in his defense before the Sanhedrin, uses the history of Israel to explain God's plan of salvation. This is the first recorded time that Israel's history has been interpreted in the light of Jesus.

The Sanhedrin has led the Jewish people to worship Moses, the law, and the temple above Jehovah. So focused are they on upholding these things given to them by God, they have rejected God Himself. In the name of God, they have murdered God. Stephen uses the very history of which they are so proud to show them their error.

✔ Read Acts 7:51-60.

What charges does Stephen level at the council?

_____

_____

What is the Sanhedrin's reaction to Stephen's defense?

_____

_____

What does Stephen see? Why do you think Jesus is standing?

_____

How does Stephen die?

_____

What is Saul doing during Stephen's stoning? Acts 7:58; 8:1

_____

The leaders of the Sanhedrin are filled with rage. Stephen uses the things they hold so dear — the law, Moses, and the temple — to prove that they are completely outside the covenant relationship with God. They drag Stephen out into the streets and out of the city gates. They then pick up stones to kill him. Their only pause is to take off their outer garments and lay them at the feet of the young Pharisee Saul. As Stephen is being stoned to death, he keeps his eyes on heaven. As a reward and comfort for his faithful testimony, God opens the curtain of heaven as Jesus stands to receive His servant. In words echoing his Lord's, Stephen asks for forgiveness for his murderers and becomes the first martyr for Christ. He speaks his final prayer as the rocks slam into his body. Stones shatter his bones, blood pours from his wounds, but nothing can break the love and faith he has in Jesus Christ. The name Stephen means, "crown." On this day, he received his crown of glory from the hand of Jesus Himself.

Write James 1:12.

_____

_____

> The same crown of righteousness placed on Stephen's head awaits you. Close your eyes and envision your crown. In a city with gold streets and pearl gates, you can be sure that your crown will be a real beauty. Feel its weight upon your head. Hear the strains of joyous music rising from the angel chorus. Catch your reflection in the light of glory. Now turn and gaze upon the One who purchased your crown with His blood. Fall on your knees and thank Him.

# DAY 2

Stephen dies as the first martyr for the name of Jesus. Through both Stephen's life and death, God is reaching out to Saul with His message of grace. The extraordinary events surrounding the death of Stephen make an imprint on the heart of young Saul. Although we do not see the fruit of Christ's seed immediately, it is the first step to breaking the hard heart that hides Saul from the grace of God.

The church in Jerusalem feels the shock waves surrounding Stephen's death immediately. Estimates have placed the number of believers at approximately 25,000 at this time.

Read Acts 8:1-4.

What happens to the Jerusalem believers?

_____

Who leads the assault against them?

_____

● How can a Christian face trials with joy? James 1:2-4

_____

_____

● In what way does the persecution by Saul fulfill God's will for the church? What does this teach you about the ways God can work through difficult circumstances?

_____

_____

● What kinds of persecution does the church face today?

_____

_____

The death of Stephen is a turning point for the church of Christ. The believers are comfortable staying in Jerusalem and to this point have not followed Jesus' command to take the gospel to Judea, Samaria, and to the ends of the earth. God uses Satan's attacks to send the gospel out of Jerusalem. Satan is wily and picks a perfect moment in history to strike at God's people. At this time, there is no Roman governor in Judea. This allows the Jewish leaders to have full authority over the region. They can deal with the followers of Jesus in any way they want without having to answer to the Romans. Leading the attack on the church is the young Pharisee Saul. His zealousness to stamp out The Way is accompanied by fury and violence.

Read Acts 26:9-11. Describe the kind of persecution Saul inflicts upon the Christians and describe his state of mind.

_____

_____

_____

Saul is going from synagogue to synagogue, and even house to house, dragging men and women to prison. Believers are beaten, interrogated, pressured to renounce the name of Jesus, and even killed. Saul, whom some believe to a member of the Sanhedrin at this time, even votes on the death sentences of many Christians. Acts 26:10

● Have you ever been persecuted for the name of Jesus? How did you handle it?

_____

_____

It is difficult for us who live in a country with such freedom to imagine a world where speaking the name of Jesus is responded to with a beating, imprisonment, and death. There are, however, many places in the world today where our Christian brothers and sisters face such persecution.

What warning does Jesus give His disciples in John 16:2?

_____

Paul later describes his state of mind at this time as being obsessed, zealous, and morally convinced that he was serving God. The phrase in Acts 8:3, *"Saul began to destroy,"* holds in it the picture of a wild animal ravaging its prey.

How does Peter describe the Christian's enemy in I Peter 5:8?

_____

● Is it possible for someone to be sincere in his beliefs and be totally separated from God? Explain.

_____

_____

While it is obvious that Paul is sincere in his belief that he is serving the Lord, his actions reveal how far he is from the heart of God. Being sincere in one's beliefs and being right with God are not synonymous. We live in a world where people think that being a "good" person is enough. Saul's experience tells us that Jesus is the only standard of righteousness by which God will measure our lives.

Write I Corinthians 4:4.

_____

_____

Why do you think Saul reacted with such viciousness to Christianity?

_____

_____

I believe that Saul saw something in Stephen's face that he has been searching for all his life — peace. Remember that Saul's entire life, his every movement from morning to night, is ruled by the Pharisees' code of oral law. Saul is sincere in his desire to approach God. He has spent his life striving to be perfect in his adherence to the Mosaic Law and the traditions of his fathers. Each day is a desperate attempt to be more perfect than the day before. In Saul's mind, failure to be perfect is failure to please God. This failure gnaws at Paul. It haunts him. His efforts create increasing turmoil as he daily faces his imperfection. Turmoil breeds anxiety and fear.

What Saul fails to understand is that it is impossible to achieve righteousness on our own.

Saul is a brilliant man and I believe he sees with great clarity the significance of the Christian message. He understands that it makes the Mosaic Law obsolete. He knows that instead of depending on their own good works, Jesus calls His followers to depend on Him. Saul realizes that the temple is no longer the primary place of worship. Priests are no longer needed to intercede for the people. Instead, through Jesus and Jesus alone, people can approach God directly. Try to understand how terrifying this is for someone who has dedicated his life to the study and adherence of the Mosaic Law. Saul sees the very fabric of his life being torn apart and reacts in defense of the way of life that defines him.

● How can fear blind us to the ways God is working in and around us?

_____

_____

# DAY 3

Stephen is dead. Fear and panic have spread through the believers in Jerusalem. Satan has launched a full-scale attack on Christ's church through the hands of Saul. When the darkness seems the most overwhelming, we are able to see the penetrating light of God most clearly. Prepare your heart to see the bright glory of His grace. Tune your ears to hear His voice. Now watch in wonder as Saul is transformed by the grace of God.

Saul is actively pursuing those who follow The Way. In his zealousness, Saul even seeks to go after those who flee Jerusalem in the wake of persecution. On one of these trips to find Jesus' followers, Paul finds Jesus.

✔ Read Acts 9:1-9, Acts 22:3-11, and Acts 26:12-18. These are parallel accounts of what happens on this amazing day. Read expectantly, slowly. Pray for God's insight and blessing as we watch God's grace reach directly into the heart of Saul.

*Locate Damascus on the map in the front of your book.*

Where is Saul going? Why?

_____

What time of day is it? What does Saul see and hear?

_____

_____

In what language does Jesus speak to Saul?

_____

What questions does Saul ask Jesus?

_____

_____

Where does Jesus tell Saul to go? How does Saul enter the city?

_____

Why is The Way a good name for the church?

_____

Saul is traveling to Damascus, a city about 150 miles from Jerusalem. It required a journey of about six days. As they approach Damascus about noon, an incredibly brilliant light surrounds the traveling party. Fear and panic spread through the men as they see the supernatural light and hear a voice they don't understand. The voice in the light speaks to only one man this day, Saul himself. This is not a vision or a trance. This is a face-to-face visit between Saul and Jesus Christ.

Write I Corinthians 15:8.

_____

● When have you felt God shine a bright light into your soul? How did you respond?

_____

_____

As He speaks to Saul, Jesus tells him that he is persecuting, not just His followers, but Him as well. The statement to Saul that he is persecuting Jesus personally holds an important truth for us.

Read I Corinthians 12:27, Ephesians 5:23, and Matthew 25:40 and record the fundamental principle about Christ and His church.

_____

_____

Saul asks the Man to identify Himself by asking, "Who are you, Lord?" Jesus replies, not that He is the Lord of Lords and King of Kings, but rather that He is Jesus of Nazareth. This simple identification confirms in Saul's mind that Jesus truly is the Messiah.

● How do you answer the question, "Who are you, Lord?"

_____

_____

Answering the question, "Who are you, Lord?" is the foundation of all faith. We must recognize that Jesus is the Son of God and that in His name only is salvation. Once you have answered the question, "Who are you, Lord?" and truly understand that Jesus is the Christ, there is only one response. "What shall I do, Lord?" This is the question that Saul asks.

Does Saul, at this moment, believe in Jesus? Is he saved because of that belief?

_____

In case there is any doubt concerning Peter's declaration on Pentecost, we have here the words of Jesus Himself regarding what is necessary for salvation. Saul's new belief in Jesus is not enough. He must go to Damascus to learn what to do. Action is required by Saul to receive his salvation.

● Why is our obedience so important to Jesus?

_____

_____

As a result of his encounter with Jesus, Saul is blind. God takes his vision so that he can learn to see more clearly. His traveling companions must now lead the arrogant, hateful Saul, who had come to Damascus to drag Christians back to Jerusalem in chains, into the city in a humiliating way.

How does Paul describe himself in Ephesians 3:1?

_____

In what way has Jesus taken the heart of Paul captive? What kind of hold does Jesus have on your heart?

_____

_____

# DAY 4

Saul and his companions were on the road to the city of Damascus to arrest and persecute followers of Jesus. On the way, Jesus Himself speaks to Saul and shines the bright light of grace into his heart revealing the blackness within. His soul stripped bare before the Lord, Saul is physically blinded in order to open his spiritual eyes. The days of darkness that lie ahead provide more illumination for Saul's soul than a lifetime of legalistic teaching.

Watch now as an ordinary man guides Saul's feet to the path of salvation.

✔ Read Acts 9:10-19 and Acts 22:12-16.

Who does God send to Saul? What is his objection?

_____

● Who has been your Ananias? To whom do you need to be an Ananias? How will you do that this week?

_____

_____

What two pieces of information does God give Saul about his new life?  Acts 9:15-16

_____

_____

How does Saul receive his sight?

_____

What does he do then?

_____

Saul is led to the house of Judas on Straight Street in Damascus. There, in the darkness, he is overwhelmed with images, emotions, and thoughts. God darkens his sight to let him see the blackness of his soul. Saul remembers the prophecies he learned as a child. He sees the bloody face of Stephen shining like an angel. He is overwhelmed with terror as he faces the filthiness of his sin. There is no more hollow, terrifying moment than looking into your own sin-soaked soul and realizing there is no way you can stand before God's holiness. In these three days, God plows through the hardened soil of Saul's heart with a sharp razor. Simultaneously, God prepares a Christian man named Ananias to go to Saul. Nowhere else in Scripture is Ananias mentioned. God doesn't send an apostle or a great evangelist to talk to Saul. He sends an ordinary man.

● What lesson do you learn from God's choice of Ananias?

_____

Ananias is, at first, skeptical of God's mission to send him to speak to Saul. Doesn't God know that Saul has come to persecute believers? God responds by telling Ananias that Saul is His chosen instrument. What an amazing thought to Ananias! The man destroying the church is God's chosen instrument for building it up! Much credit goes to Ananias. When God said, "Go," Ananias lays down his fear and goes.

It is humbling to watch as Ananias sets out to deliver God's message of grace to Saul. God could have sent anyone – an apostle or an evangelist. Rather He sends a simple, ordinary man to bring Saul Christ's extraordinary message. What we often fail to understand is that the power is in the message, not the messenger. So many times we feel inadequate to tell others about His grace. Telling others the good news doesn't require great eloquence or a graduate education. All it requires is a heart that has been touched by His love and transformed by His grace.

Ananias goes to the room where Saul is staying and places his hands on the one who had come to place him in chains. There was never a sweeter moment of brotherly love, a more tender word to Saul's ear than when Ananias calls him brother. Because God has embraced him, Ananias embraces him as well.

Ananias lays his hands on Saul and his vision returns. Now he sees the world in a whole new light — the light of God's love.

Write Ananias' words in Acts 22:16.

_____

_____

 That is just what Saul does. He is immersed in baptism and into the grace of God. The world has never been the same.

I want to plead with you. If you have not been baptized into the name of Jesus, what are you waiting for? There is no other moment so precious, no other moment so urgent as the one you have right now. The grace of God is extended to you at this moment. Accept His love, be baptized into His name and the world will never be the same.

If you are a Christian baptized into the blood of Jesus, I plead with you as well. Search your heart and reclaim your dependence on the righteousness of Jesus Christ. It is so easy to be content with your own goodness, but it will make your heart hard. Have the courage of Ananias. We all know someone who needs the gentle touch of God's grace. It requires courage and laying aside your fear. But if you go, the world will never be the same.

● In practical terms, how do we daily keep ourselves dependent on the blood of Jesus? What freedom does this give us? What responsibilities?

_____

_____

# Grace Sent Out

Last week we witnessed the miracle of God's grace as Persecutor Saul became Brother Saul. Saul, however, does not immediately set out on the missionary journeys for which he is so famous. Rather, the next decade of the apostle's life is spent in relative obscurity. What does Saul do during this time? Where does he go? What are God's lessons during this time of relative quiet? These are some of the questions we explore as we watch God prepare Saul for His service.

## DAY 1

The details of these approximately nine to ten years in the life of Saul are sketchy. They must be pieced together from clues given by Luke in the book of Acts and in the apostle's letters. Despite the lack of information about this time, do not underestimate its importance in Saul's spiritual growth. God uses this time to train, teach, and temper Saul.

Below is a reasonable timeline of Saul's activities during this time.

Spent a few days with the disciples in Damascus.   Acts 9:19b

Went into Arabia    Galatians 1:17

Returned to Damascus/preached in synagogues    Acts 9:20-25

Visited Peter in Jerusalem    Acts 9:26-29; Galatians 1:18-20

Returned to Tarsus    Acts 9:30; Galatians 1:21-24

Read Acts 9:19b. What does Saul do after his conversion?

_____

After his baptism, Saul spends a few refreshing days with the Christians in Damascus. The very people he had come to arrest and torture welcome him into their homes and hearts. This hospitality must have been a soothing balm to the soul freshly released from its chains of sin.

 Read Galatians 1:11-17.

Where does Saul go after his conversion?

_____

Why is this information important to his authority as an apostle?

_____

_____

With whom does he speak in Arabia?

_____

After the amazing days surrounding his conversion to faith in Jesus, Saul needs time to contemplate his new life and spend time in prayer talking to his Lord. While there is no record, it is entirely consistent to believe that Jesus Himself called Saul into the desert.

Read the following and note where Saul got his knowledge of the gospel.
Galatians 1:1,16; I Corinthians 11:23

_____

Now read Ephesians 3:6-12 and record what he learned.

_____

_____

The authority for Saul's apostleship and his intimate knowledge of the gospel does not come from men, but from God Himself. He does not present himself to the apostles for approval nor does he seek their understanding of the good news. Jesus makes sure that Saul has everything he needs to fulfill his role as apostle to the Gentiles.

What promises are made to you concerning your ability to fulfill God's will in your life?

I Corinthians 12:6 _____

II Corinthians 9:8 _____

Ephesians 3:20 _____

Philippians 2:13 _____

Hebrews 13:20-21 _____

● In what way has God equipped you for His work? Why?

_____

_____

> In the same way He equipped Paul, He will equip you and me for His glory.

✔ Read Acts 9:20-25.

After Saul's sojourn in Arabia, he returns to Damascus. What does Saul do there?

_____

What is the people's response to his teaching?

_____

What does Saul prove through his teaching?

_____

What is the reaction of the Jewish leadership? How does Saul escape them?

_____

_____

The joy and zeal for Jesus in the heart of Saul cannot be silent for long. Immediately upon his return to Damascus, full of the Holy Spirit, Saul begins proclaiming the name of Jesus in the Jewish synagogues. The people are dumbfounded. They know Saul's reputation, and the sight of the transformed persecutor of The Way to a now outspoken advocate of its cause is astonishing.

It is difficult to explain the shock waves that went through the Jewish hierarchy at the defection of one of their brightest stars. Imagine waking up in 1945 and the headline in the morning paper reads "HITLER MARRIES JEW." The thought of Saul becoming a believer in Jesus is equally unimaginable for the Jews. They are horrified. Yet instead of Saul's conversion convincing them to reexamine the facts, they resort to their standard solution of killing the problem.

Saul and the Damascus Christians learn of their evil plot. In II Corinthians 11:32, Saul tells us that the king of Damascus went so far as to post guards all around the city to arrest him. He escapes, however, by being lowered through an opening in the wall in a basket.

● What did Saul give up when he chose to become a Christian? What have you given up for the name of Christ?

_____

_____

# DAY 2

It has been three years since Saul's conversion. Now on the run from the Jewish leaders in Damascus, Saul makes the decision to go to Jerusalem. It takes a lot of courage to walk from the lion's den into the lion's mouth!

✔ Read Acts 9:26-29 and Galatians 1:18-19.

Why does Saul go to Jerusalem? How do other Christians receive him?

_____

_____

Who introduces him to the apostles? How long does he spend with Peter?

_____

Saul goes to Jerusalem and spends fifteen days. Imagine Saul's thoughts as the walls of Jerusalem appear on the horizon. He sees the ancient temple in a new light. He remembers his arrogance and hatred toward his now beloved brothers and sisters in Christ. His ears ring with the sound of rocks as they hit Stephen's body. He left Jerusalem willing to kill those who belonged to Jesus. He now enters Jerusalem willing to die for that name.

If the Jews are furious about Saul's new faith, the Jerusalem Christians are suspicious of its sincerity. Remember these men and women have seen their loved ones, perhaps have even themselves been persecuted by this man who now seeks to come into their midst. Thank God for Barnabas! Barnabas puts his arm around his new brother and believes his story of God's grace. Barnabas takes Saul and introduces him to Peter.

● Does the church today need people like Barnabas? Why?

_____

_____

● In what way has someone been a Barnabas to you? How can you be a Barnabas?

_____

_____

> The first century church, and we today, would not have the blessings of Paul had it not been for quiet men like Ananias and Barnabas.

Saul is received into the Christian family and spends time with Peter and Jesus' brother James. They must spend hours talking about Jesus, His ministry, His death and resurrection, and His special call to each of them. Saul tells of his days of darkness and Peter remembers of his denials. Each uniquely understands the blessedness of forgiveness.

Amidst the teaching he does daily in the synagogues and his visits with Peter, Saul finds time for a special trip to the temple.

✔ Read Acts 22:17-21.

What is Saul doing in the temple? What happens there?

_____

What instructions does Jesus give Saul? How does he respond?

_____

_____

This is the third time Jesus tells Saul that he will be His ambassador to the Gentiles. Saul tries to argue, saying that the change in his life is a powerful testimony to the Jews. His heart's desire is to save the people of his birth. God, however, has other plans for Saul.

● Have you ever wanted to serve God one way but been directed another? Explain.

_____

_____

As in Damascus, the Jewish leadership cannot tolerate Saul's explosive testimony concerning Jesus and the resurrection. They once again seek to take his life.

✔ Read Acts 9:29-31 and Galatians 1:21-24.

Where do the Christians in Jerusalem send Saul?

_____

They send Saul home to Tarsus. Like Saul, we too need time to grow in our faith and Christian walk.

 Read Ephesians 4:11-16.

What term is used to describe new Christians?

_____

Paul uses the term infants to describe new Christians. This provides us with a good picture for understanding spiritual growth and maturity. This passage and this time in Saul's life give us four interlocking steps to take *"to grow up into him who is the Head, that is, Christ."* Ephesians 4:15

**Step 1: Fill yourself with God's word.**

As every new mom learns, babies are born hungry! They need to be fed in order to thrive. The same thing is true in our growth as Christians. We must continually feed our hearts and souls on the word of God.

Write I Peter 2:2.

_____

_____

 Spiritual hunger is a sign of spiritual health. When one of my children is sick, the first question the doctor asks is about their appetite. Only a sick child has no appetite. Lack of spiritual hunger is a warning sign of spiritual sickness! We need to develop a taste for the deeper things of God.

**Step 2: Fellowship with other Christians.**

Besides being fed, the other thing babies need is to be held. We hear tragic stories of babies in hospitals and orphanages being developmentally delayed and even dying because they lack human contact. In the same way, we need regular contact with other Christians to grow in Jesus.

Read Ephesians 4:16. Who is involved in the growth process?

_____

 The whole body! You cannot cut yourself off from the church of Christ and expect to grow.

**Step 3: Prayer.**

Infants learn the language of their parents by spending time in interactive communication. Prayer is two-way communication between you and your Heavenly Father. It is through prayer that we develop intimacy with God. Prayer helps us bind our hearts to His and lets us understand His specific will for our lives.

● Write I Thessalonians 5:17. How do we do this?

_____

_____

**Step 4: Work in the Lord's body.**

This one may seem a little surprising but the principle is fundamental and sound.

How does the whole body grow and build itself up in love? Ephesians 4:16

_____

One of the key elements of spiritual growth is rolling up your sleeves and getting your hands dirty in the work of the Lord. Many people say they can't work for the church because they are not spiritually mature. You can't become spiritually mature unless you work!

We understand this principle in our families.

● Why do we give children chores to do?

_____

_____

These are the same reasons we are to do "chores" in the church. Without the work, we will never know the satisfaction of service, the joy of belonging, the pride of accomplishment, and the sacrifice of love.

● How are you implementing these four steps in your Christian walk?

_____

_____

Saul spends the next four to five years in obscurity. Ten years is a long to time to wait. God, however, is molding a man who must learn to trust His power, His timing, His leading, and His grace completely to finish the task before him.

Perhaps God has you waiting now as well. Don't think of this as wasted time. God wants you to use this time to become more attuned to His voice, more softened to His will, more thirsty for His love. Prepare yourself well. You never know what task He has for you around the corner!

## DAY 3

Saul spends four to five years in the area of Cilicia following his departure from Jerusalem. During this time the word of God has been almost exclusively preached to the Jews. The time is now ripe for the Gentiles to be brought full force into the family of God.

*Locate Antioch on the map in the front of your book.*

✔ Read Acts 11:19-30.

What begins to happen at Antioch?

_____

Who is sent from Jerusalem to investigate? What does he discover?

_____

_____

● By what evidence does Barnabas examine the work at Antioch? What evidence of the grace of God can others see in you?

_____

_____

● In what ways does Barnabas help these new Christians grow in the Lord? What can we learn from Barnabas' example?

_____

_____

Of whom does Barnabas go in search? Why?

_____

_____

By what name are the disciples first known in Antioch?

_____

As the church scatters because of the persecution associated with the death of Stephen, the believers carry their message of Jesus with them. Up to this point, the followers of Jesus have not separated themselves from Judaism. They are seen as just another sect of Jews, like the Pharisees or Saducees. In Antioch, however, Hellenists (Greek-speaking Jews) begin to share the gospel with their Greek friends. Great numbers of Gentiles are baptized and added to the church at Antioch. Hearing of the great success, the church in Jerusalem sends Barnabas to investigate. Similar to Stephen, Barnabas is described as *"a good man, full of the Holy Spirit and faith."* What a wonderful legacy! We should all desire to be recognized in such a way.

When Barnabas arrives, he is immediately impressed with the work of the Spirit in Antioch. He stays to encourage them and continue the strengthening of God's work. The addition of the Gentiles, however, brings some unique problems to Antioch. The tearing down of the walls of prejudice is difficult work. As Barnabas works in Antioch, he is reminded of his friend Saul and the unusual call to be the apostle to the Gentiles he had received from God.

Barnabas sets out for Tarsus. What Saul has been doing during these years is unknown. Had his family rejected him? Had he suffered hardship at the hands of the Jews? Whatever he did, it must have been a day of gladness when Barnabas' shadow darkens the door of Saul's home. He does not hesitate to join Barnabas in the work at Antioch. Barnabas and Saul spend the next year working with the church at Antioch. Their work brings a bountiful harvest of believers.

One of the evidences of the grace of God that we see in this place is an outpouring of the generosity that so characterizes the early church. The year is 44 AD and a famine is plaguing the land. The church at Antioch sees the opportunity to help their Jerusalem brothers and sisters who are being so challenged by persecution. It is likely that many of the Christians in Jerusalem have been cut off from family and jobs as a result of their faith. The Antioch church sends Barnabas and Saul to carry the gift.

Read Acts 12:25. Who accompanies Barnabas and Saul back to Antioch?

_____

● What does the name Christian mean to you?

_____

*"The disciples were first called Christians at Antioch."* Acts 11:26 What a beautiful name! The fact that this special name is introduced here is no coincidence. Many believe that this name was given to the believers at Antioch as a name of mockery. However, it seems unlikely that Satan would choose a name that so honored Jesus. The Jews would have never given this name to the believers because the name Christ is the Greek equivalent of Messiah. The name Christian would indicate that they were the followers of the Messiah and this the Jews could not admit. Rather, the Jews referred to them as the *"Nazarene sect"* Acts 24:5 They used the phrase Nazarene because of the old saying that "nothing good could come out of Nazareth." John 1:46 They called the followers of Christ a sect because they wanted them under the authority of the Jewish leaders.

The name Christian means "of Christ." As the believers in Antioch struggle with their new identity, it becomes imperative for God to separate them from the Jewish faith. I believe God gives this new name to the believers at Antioch.

A new name had been promised and prophesied by God in the Old Testament.

 Read Isaiah 62:1-2.

When was the name to be given? Who would bestow the name?

_____

The new name was to be given after two things had happened. First, the appearance of Jerusalem's righteousness and salvation. There is not a more beautiful description of the work of Jesus. The second prerequisite was the nations seeing that righteousness. That did not happen until the Gentiles were included into the church at Antioch. When the widespread dissemination of the gospel to the Gentiles began, God granted them a new name — Christians.[1]

 Read Isaiah 56:5.

How long is the new name supposed to last?

_____

In this passage, Isaiah is speaking of a time when those who were once cut off from the worship of God would be included. He says that within this new temple, which is the Christian heart, God would give them a new, everlasting name. The fulfillment of Isaiah's prophecy is found here in Acts 11.

How are we to wear that name? I Peter 4:16

_____

With praise!

# DAY 4

Saul is working among the Christians in Antioch. God will now use the church at Antioch as a platform to launch the first organized mission trip to the world. Let's put on our walking shoes and go with Saul as he sets out to take the grace of God throughout the world.

Read Acts 13:1-3 and see how Barnabas and Saul are chosen to go spread the gospel.

What are the leaders of Antioch called to do by the Holy Spirit?

_____

_____

● What does the phrase *"set apart"* mean? Is this something we should do today? What in your life do you need to set apart or dedicate to the Lord? Why?

_____

_____

While focused on God in worship, the Holy Spirit directs the leadership of Antioch to set apart Barnabas and Saul for special work. God is now ready to send Saul out to the Gentiles around the world.

During the last few years, Saul has learned to lean on the leading of the Spirit, to more fully understand the gospel, to see God's desire to offer the invitation of Christ to Jews and Gentiles alike. He is more mature, more committed to the full expansion of the gospel, more aware of the grace of God. God has prepared His servant and the servant is ready to go.

After a period of fasting and prayer, the church of Antioch sends Barnabas and Saul on their way. They lay their hands on them to indicate the special purpose to which they have been called and to unite themselves in the mission of the Spirit.

From this point on, I encourage you to follow the map in the front of your workbook. Use a pencil or marker to trace the route that Paul takes in the years ahead.

✔ Read Acts 13:4-12 as Barnabas and Saul set out on their first missionary journey.

Who sends these men on this trip?

_____

*On the map in the front of your book, mark the path described in verses 4-6.*

What two important people do they meet in Paphos?

_____

Describe Sergius Paulus.

_____

Describe Bar-Jesus. What is his other name?

_____

Who takes the lead in this encounter? Why?

_____

What miracle does Paul do here? Why? What is the result?

_____

_____

While the Antioch church has dispatched Barnabas and Saul, we are clearly told that the Holy Spirit is the travel agent for this group.

The group sets sail from Seleucia, which is the harbor for Antioch. It is located about sixteen miles downstream from Antioch itself. From Seleucia, the gospel preachers sail for the island of Cyprus. As Barnabas is the leader of the group and from Cyprus, it is a natural place to begin. They arrive at Salamis on the eastern slopes of Cyprus, a journey of about 100 miles. They proclaim the name of Jesus in the synagogues, but there is no record of reaping a harvest there.

From Salamis, Barnabas and Saul travel through the entire island of Cyprus until they reach Paphos on its west coast, another journey of approximately 100 miles. Paphos is the Roman headquarters on Cyprus and the center of the worship of Aphrodite.

In Paphos, Barnabas and Saul come to the attention of the Roman proconsul, Sergius Paulus. The proconsul is an intelligent man interested in hearing the word of God being preached by Barnabas and Saul.

The Holy Spirit's attention is, however, more focused on the opponent that stands at the proconsul's side. Bar-Jesus is Jewish and perhaps had come to the proconsul's attention as he sought to learn about God. Once at the proconsul's side, however, his influence as a sorcerer and false prophet become apparent. He is even given the name Elymas, which means sorcerer. The audience room of Sergius Paulus becomes a battleground between God and Satan.

Elymas tries at every turn to defeat the gospel and ruin the influence of the Holy Spirit. At this obvious attack by Satan on the message of Jesus, Saul becomes the general. Using his Roman name in this Roman place, Paul, once the messenger of Satan's persecution of the church, becomes the instrument of Satan's defeat in this place.

Paul, with a mere change of his name, sheds the life he had and the name Satan had used to destroy the church. He embraces God's destiny for his life as the apostle of grace to the Gentiles. Paul is neither subtle nor reserved in his attack on Satan's servant Elymas. What he sees as evil, he calls evil.

● What in your world do you need to stand up and oppose as evil?

_____

 We need to have the courage of Paul. Our world is filled with evil and we should not hesitate to identify evil by its true name. It is politically correct to say that there is no evil, just alternative choices. We as Christians are called to shine as a light on the darkness of evil, not only to expose it, but also to provide an opportunity for repentance.

Perhaps remembering the dramatic impact his own blindness had on him in Damascus, Paul tells Elymas that he will be as physically blind as he is spiritually blind. Luke shows us his training as a doctor in this verse by describing the blindness in the medical terminology used by Greek physicians to describe cataracts.

The result of the confrontation between Sergius Paulus' advisor Elymas and Paul is belief in Jesus by the Roman proconsul. The word belief should be understood to include all that is necessary to attain salvation. How exciting for Barnabas and Paul to have brought a man to Christ who has such political power!

 Read Acts 13:13.

 *On the map in the front of the book, mark the route described in verse 13.*

Who leaves the travel group in Perga? What other change do you notice?

_____

From Paphos, Paul and his company sail back to the mainland. Notice the shift in leadership. When they set sail, it was Barnabas who was the leader; now it is Paul. The burden and honor of taking the gospel to the Gentiles rests squarely on the shoulders of Paul. Without Barnabas, however, Paul could never have become the man we study today. There is a whole generation of young Christians who are crying out for leadership and guidance from the older and more mature in our church family. There are very few who are called to be Pauls, but many of us are called to be like Barnabas. It does not take much more than open eyes and an open heart to put your arm around a younger sister in Christ and be an "encourager." (Remember, that is what the name Barnabas means.) It is not only our privilege, but our responsibility to serve and train those younger in the faith than ourselves.

Define your responsibility as laid out by Paul in Titus 2:3-5.

_____

_____

● Why are we give the responsibility to teach each other, woman-to-woman? In what have you accepted this responsibility?

_____

_____


● What are some practical ways you can implement this responsibility?

_____

_____

> I know no one wants to admit to being the "older woman," but we are all older in some experience or lesson of faith than someone else. I challenge you to find a sister who needs a word of encouragement and give it to her. Take her along on your journey of faith. Don't abandon your responsibility to the "younger women." It will be a blessing not only to her but also to you.


As we close our lesson this week we must take note of the departure of one of Paul's traveling companions. John Mark goes home to Jerusalem. We are not told the reason he left. Perhaps it is the change in leadership from Barnabas to Paul, perhaps the strains of travel, perhaps the mixed reception the gospel receives, or perhaps just homesickness. Whatever the reason, John Mark leaves Paul and Barnabas in Pamphylia.

You are doing an excellent job! I pray you are catching a glimpse of the excitement that fills the heart of Paul as he travels the world proclaiming the grace of God. Keep up the good work. The days ahead are only more exciting and filled with greater blessing.

---

1 Coffman, *Acts,* p234-236

# Bold Grace

Last week, we left Paul and Barnabas in Perga, the capital of Pamphylia. Today we continue to walk with Paul and his companions as they travel the region of Galatia to Pisidian Antioch. At every turn there are great opportunities to preach the good news of Jesus. Our heroes will also face stern opposition as they boldly proclaim the grace of God. Put on your walking shoes. Here we go!

## DAY 1

✔ Read Acts 13:14-43.

*On the map in the front of your book, mark the route taken by Paul in verse 14.*

Where do Paul and Barnabas go after leaving Perga? Where do they go once in the city?

_____

Outline the four main points of Paul's sermon.

1.                                    2.

3.                                    4.

Why does Paul go to the synagogue first if he was sent to preach to the Gentiles?

_____

_____

What is the reaction of the people listening?

_____

_____

● How does the worship in the synagogue prepare the people to listen to Paul's message about Jesus? Acts 13:15  How do you prepare your heart to see Jesus?

_____

_____

Paul and Barnabas travel about 110 miles inland from Perga to Pisidian Antioch. This is not the same Antioch from which they left, which is known as Syrian Antioch. Pisidian Antioch is well situated on the trade routes of Asia Minor and is a Roman colony settled by retired Roman soldiers. There is an active synagogue in the city and this provides the starting point for Paul's ministry in this area.

On the Sabbath, Paul and Barnabas go to the synagogue. After the reading of the Law and the Prophets, it is customary to invite traveling teachers to make comments to the assembly. This gives Paul an extraordinary opportunity. In every city to which Paul travels, he always begins in the synagogue. Not only does this provide Paul with an audience educated in the Old Testament, it is cemented in God's revealed plan for spreading the message of salvation.

Write Romans 1:16.

_____

_____

_____

Paul's address to the people assembled in the synagogue holds out four main ideas.

*The history of Israel points to the coming Messiah.* Paul reviews the history of Israel in much the same way as Peter and Stephen. He specifically points back to the promises made to King David. All Jews understand David to be a foreshadow of the Messiah.

What about David's character was most important to God?

_____

● How do we develop this kind of heart?

_____

*God sent a messenger to prepare the people for His coming.* The Jews know that the coming of the Messiah would be proceeded by the *"voice of one calling: 'In the desert prepare the way for the Lord.'"* Isaiah 40:3 Paul tells them that John the Baptist had fulfilled this mission. He uses the ministry of John the Baptist as proof that this and other Old Testament prophecies are fulfilled in Jesus.

● In what way is the gospel of Jesus a *"message of encouragement"*? Acts 13:15 With whom do you need to share the message of encouragement?

_____

_____

*The miraculous facts of the life, death, and resurrection of Jesus.* Paul presents the facts of the ministry of Jesus and the miraculous events surrounding His death, burial, and resurrection. He points to the witnesses that can testify to their truth. He ends by again showing from the Scriptures how Jesus is the promised Messiah.

● In what way is the story of Jesus *"good news"* for your life? Acts 13:32

_____

_____

*Paul asks the people to make a decision. Forgiveness or judgment lie before them.* The message of the resurrection of Jesus is in its substance, a call to grace. Sin lies between man and God. The blood of Jesus is the only avenue for forgiveness. It is not enough to gaze at the pool of blood. We must make a committed decision to enter into that blood through baptism.

✔ Read Deuteronomy 30:11-20.

How does Moses define your choice?

_____

● How close is your choice?

_____

● What is your choice?

_____

Luke gives us this outline of Paul's sermon as a general model of the sermons he preaches at each synagogue. Let's take note of an interesting fact for which I would like you to continue watching as we go on our journey with the apostle Paul. The heart of Paul, every conversation he has, every sermon that he preaches, every miracle that he performs, focuses on one thing — the resurrection of Jesus Christ. Every time. All hope, all grace, all power, all strength, all forgiveness, all peace is found in that one truth. I wonder what power the church would have today if we proclaimed the resurrection of Jesus with the same intensity.

● In what way is your life a testimony to the resurrection of Jesus?

_____

_____

# DAY 2

Yesterday, Paul and Barnabas entered the city of Pisidian Antioch and set out to preach the gospel of grace in the local synagogue. An amazing thing happens as Paul and Barnabas leave the synagogue. He is invited back to preach the same sermon the next week! In fact, the people press in around Paul asking to hear more about the grace of God.

✔ Read Acts 13:44-52.

How many people come to the next gospel meeting?

_____

How do the Jews react? How do the Gentiles react?

_____

✔ Read II Corinthians 2:14-16.

What are we to God? What does God do through us?  Explain the two reactions to this fragrance.

_____

_____

We, as Christians, are the sweet aroma of Christ before God. Our lives, service, and love for Jesus are the fragrance that God spreads throughout the world to proclaim the good news of the gospel. As the world inhales the scent of our lives, there will be two dramatic reactions. To those entombed in sin, with their hearts hard to God's grace, the aroma of Christ brings forth the smell of death. Have you ever smelled death? We react violently to death's stench. Such is the vile odor of sin. To those open to the good news of Jesus, we are the fragrance of life. What do you do when surrounded by a lovely aroma? We inhale deeply, absorbing every morsel of its sweetness. Either way, our life in Christ causes a profound reaction in the world around us.

● What reaction does your life cause among those you meet?

_____

● What does it mean if we are not causing a reaction?

_____

What action do the Jews take against Paul?

_____

_____

● Why are the Jews' hearts so hard to the gospel of Christ? What warning is there for us in their attitude?

_____

_____

What do Paul and Barnabas do as they leave town?

_____

Why are the disciples filled with joy?

_____

_____

✔ Read Acts 13:38 and Acts 3:19.

● In what way does the forgiveness of Jesus refresh you? How are you making time to daily soak in that refreshment?

_____

_____

Word spreads quickly through Pisidian Antioch about the message preached by Paul. The next Sabbath day, almost the entire city shows up at the synagogue to hear the word of God. Of course, this crowd is made up of not only Jews, but a large number of Gentiles as well. The Jewish leadership, instead of rejoicing at the spread of God's love, become filled with jealousy and started verbally attacking Paul.

● Have you ever been verbally attacked because of your faith? How did you handle it?

_____

_____

✔ Read I Peter 3:14-16.

● How are we to respond to those who attack our faith?

_____

_____

It is easy for the church today to become inwardly focused. We get absorbed in thinking about our meetings, program, and members. To bring in people who make us uncomfortable disrupts us and makes us nervous. It is easier to be with people who are like us. The example we have, however, is of a church that is ever outward going in its spread of the gospel. We must be careful not to become like the Jewish leaders here who so zealously guard God's love that they cannot share it.

● Who is someone with whom you might be uncomfortable sharing the gospel?

_____

Paul and Barnabas boldly answer the Jews. I like that word "boldly." They are not intimidated because someone disagrees with them. They call upon the Spirit of God to make them bold. They announce that they have fulfilled their obligation to the gospel by coming to the Jews first, but the message of God is now available to the Gentiles.

This same boldness shown by Paul is available to you. The blood of Jesus allows us confidence before God and men.

Write Hebrews 4:16.

_____

_____

_____

● How does having this kind of confidence help us face difficult circumstances?

_____

_____

The Gentiles, in contrast to the Jews, receive the word with great joy. Many Gentiles believe in Jesus, are baptized, and receive eternal life this day. In protest to the resistance that they encounter from the Jews, Paul and Barnabas shake off the dust from their feet. Yet despite the opposition from the Jews, the disciples are filled with joy. A new church of Jesus Christ has been planted and many have believed and been saved. Any day like that is a day for rejoicing!

# DAY 3

Paul and Barnabas are traveling through the region of Galatia on their first missionary journey. They have already stood before a sorcerer and felt the arrows of Satan's attacks. They have seen the bitterness and hardheartedness of the Jews swell into jealousy and rebellion. And the journey is only half over! Today we will watch as Satan's attacks become more vicious and Paul's heart more courageous.

✔ Read Galatians 4:13-15.

At some point during this journey through Galatia, Paul becomes ill. What opportunity does Paul's illness provide?

_____

● Have you experienced an illness or difficult circumstance that has provided you an opportunity to share your faith? Explain.

_____

_____

What is the reaction of the people?

_____

_____

What part of Paul's body is affected by the illness?

_____

The letter to the Galatians is written to the Christians that Paul is now teaching on this first missionary journey. Pisidian Antioch, Iconium, Lystra, and Derbe are all in the region designated by Rome as Galatia.

Despite his illness, or perhaps because of it, Paul is able to effectively preach to the people about the love of God. The illness apparently has some ill effects on the apostle's eyes.

Isn't it interesting that Paul uses the occasion of his illness to tend to the needs of others through the gospel? When we are sick, we usually use it as an excuse to be relieved of church obligations. I have known, however, some wonderful Christians who have used their lengthy battles with cancer and such diseases as a pedestal for the love of Jesus. May we see opportunities to shine the light of Jesus in all our circumstances!

● How do we learn to see every circumstance as an opportunity to share Jesus?

_____

_____

✔ Read Acts 14:1-7.

📜 *On the map in the front of your book, mark the route taken by Paul in verse 1.*

Traveling about ninety miles through mountainous country, Paul and Barnabas arrive at Iconium.

Where does Paul begin his preaching? What is the result?

_____

_____

How are Paul and Barnabas able to counter the "poisoning" of the people?

_____

● Why is it necessary for God to confirm the message of Paul and Barnabas with miraculous signs?

_____

_____

Why do they leave Iconium?

_____

As is his pattern, Paul begins his teaching in Iconium at the local synagogue. There is a large group of Jews at this place and a great number of both Jews and Gentiles respond to the gospel. At every turn, however, Paul meets the extreme resistance of the Jews.

This continual attack on Paul and the gospel of Jesus causes Paul great personal pain. He is very proud of the advantages he has because of his Jewish background. He had spent his early life learning and studying all that was important to the Hebrews. He desperately longs for the Jews to see the Messiah. He knows that God's judgment on the Jewish nation is near and that only by turning to Jesus can Israel be saved.

Write Romans 9:2-3.

_____

_____

_____

● What kind of passion does Paul have for the lost? How do we develop that kind of passion?

_____

_____

Every time the Jews reject the message of Jesus, Paul feels a stab of pain in his heart.

Here again the Jews reject the grace of God and set out to poison the minds of the people against Paul and Barnabas. The Holy Spirit, however, allows them to do great numbers of miraculous signs to confirm their message to the people. This gives the brothers in Christ boldness and they stay in Iconium for some time.

As is always the case with the message of Jesus, eventually the town is divided — some on the side of Paul, and some on the side of the Jews. Paul and his companions find out about a plan by the leadership of the town to abuse and stone them and they escape to Lystra and Derbe in the area of Lycaonia.

Jesus said there is no middle ground when it comes to the kingdom of God. You are either for Him or against Him. There is no one who can say they are undecided or they don't care. You have either responded in obedience through baptism to the Lamb or you have not. The side of Jesus or the side of Satan. Choose your side carefully. It is the difference between victory and defeat, life and death.

## DAY 4

In Iconium, Paul and Barnabas encounter the hard hearts of the Jews. They are forced to leave the city as rejection and violence swirl around them. From Iconium, the travelers move east approximately eighteen to twenty miles to Lystra where they encounter a very different kind of resistance.

✔ Read Acts 14:8-20.

*Mark on the map in the front of your book the route taken by Paul in verse 6.*

Describe the man Paul encounters in Lystra.

_____

What does Paul do for this man? What is the reaction of the people?

_____

_____

What is the reaction of Paul and Barnabas?

_____

_____

Who comes to stir up trouble for the men of God?

_____

What happens to Paul? Do you see anything miraculous in this event?

_____

_____

Evidently the Jewish population is very small for there is no record of a synagogue in Lystra. As Paul talks about Jesus in Lystra, he becomes aware of a man who has been lame since birth. With the insight of the Holy Spirit, Paul sees the man's faith and heals him. The man doesn't just get up, the text says he *"jumped up."* God doesn't do things halfway!

● How does the healing of the lame man picture the message of the gospel?

_____

● What is the beginning of our spiritual renewal? In your own words (without quoting Scripture), define faith. Why is our faith important to God?

_____

_____

Write Hebrews 11:6.

_____

_____

The plight of the lame man mirrors the condition of us all. We are spiritual cripples unable to stand before God. There is no way for us to heal ourselves. Only in the name of Jesus do we find the cure that frees us from our disease.

When we walk into the name of Jesus through baptism, we are healed of the sin that cripples our souls. We can enter into God's presence with jumping and joy and praise.

Outside of the gates of the city of Lystra is a temple dedicated to the worship of Zeus. Zeus is the chief god in the Greek pantheon and Hermes is his messenger. These are the gods worshipped by the people of Lystra. The healing of a man crippled since birth astonishes and amazes the crowd. An old legend holds that these gods had visited the city in the ancient days and the people now believe that Zeus and Hermes have returned in the images of Paul and Barnabas. They name Barnabas Zeus because, in eastern cultures, the one who does not speak is the most powerful. Paul they name Hermes because he is the spokesperson of the group.

The people begin preparations to worship Paul and Barnabas. They make ready bulls and garlands under the leadership of the priest of Zeus. When Paul and Barnabas learn of the sacrifices and worship the people are preparing, they are stunned and horrified. They rip their clothes in anguish and rush into the crowd pleading with them not to do such a blasphemous thing. Paul, in particular, begs the people to put away their idols and worship the living God. They finally succeed in annulling the sacrifices, but not without much difficulty.

● What kinds of "gods" do people in our society seek to worship? What kinds of sacrifices do they make?

_____

_____

Amazingly enough, Jews from as far away as Pisidian Antioch come to Lystra to stir up trouble for Paul. Understand, there are no superhighways or airplanes for travel. These trouble-making Jews travel over 100 miles through very rough country on foot or animals to stir up dissension against Paul. They are certainly committed to defeating the gospel! May we be that committed to proclaiming it. One day the people are ready to worship Paul and the next they are ready to kill him. They pick up stones and pelt the apostle's body until they think he is dead. They then drag his limp, broken, bloody body out of the city for the carrion to feast on. Imagine the images that go through Paul's mind as the stones began to fly. I imagine he vividly sees the face of Stephen, remembering again his guilt, but also now understanding the peace on Stephen's face. The man who had killed because of the gospel is now ready to die for the gospel. Only God could make such a remarkable transformation in a man's heart. As the Christians from the city gather around, Paul gets up and walks back into the city. God intervenes in the life of Paul healing him of those injuries. God is not finished with His apostle.

Before we leave Lystra, we must introduce ourselves to a family who is most certainly among those standing around Paul's bloody body outside the city gates. The eyes and heart of one young man in particular are deeply impacted by the love of Jesus he sees Paul carrying in his heart.

Read Acts 16:1 to learn the name of this young man.

_____

● Paul has the eyes of young Timothy on him. What young eyes are watching your daily Christian walk? What are you teaching them about Jesus?

_____

_____

Despite the stoning received by Paul, he is capable of traveling the next day. As the sun rises, Paul and Barnabas set out for the town of Derbe, about sixty miles away. This is the last stop in the journey. Going any farther would take them into the region of Cilicia. The missionaries receive an excellent response in Derbe and then proceed to retrace their steps.

✔ Read Acts 14:21-28.

*On the map in the front of your book, mark the route taken by Paul in verses 20, 21, 24-26.*

What do Paul and Barnabas do as they revisit each of these cities?

_____

_____

● How do you think Paul and Barnabas strengthened and encouraged the disciples? How can you strengthen and encourage some of God's people today?

_____

_____

Despite the hateful Jews and the persecution they have seen in each city, Paul and Barnabas revisit each group of new Christians to encourage and strengthen them. They explain that enduring hardship is to be expected for the name of Jesus.

✔ Read II Timothy 3:10-12.

What can we expect as followers of Jesus? Why?

_____

_____

Also on this return journey they seek to establish leaders among each group of Christians. This is the first time we see the appointing of elders in the church. The elders are instrumental in maintaining and strengthening the faith of the Christians in each city as well as overseeing the spread of the gospel in the area.

● Look at the following and note some of the responsibilities of elders.

I Timothy 5:17 _____

I Peter 5:1-4 _____

Acts 20:28 _____

Titus 1:7-9 _____

Elders are just as vital in the church today. Throughout the New Testament, these men are held up as the authority, under Christ, for the local body. Being an elder is not a position of power, but a position of service. Take a moment this week to seek out your elders and thank them for the work they do for you.

Finally Paul and his companions return home to Antioch. They have much wonderful news to tell of the work of God among the Gentiles. Tired but exhilarated by the door God has opened before them, Paul takes time to refresh himself among the Christians he loves so much. God refills Paul's spirit because soon he will be called again to *"carry my name before the Gentiles."*

● Looking back over this missionary journey, Paul and Barnabas have traveled over 1,000 miles spreading God's grace. What have you learned about Paul? About God? In what ways have they challenged you in your journey of faith?

_____

_____

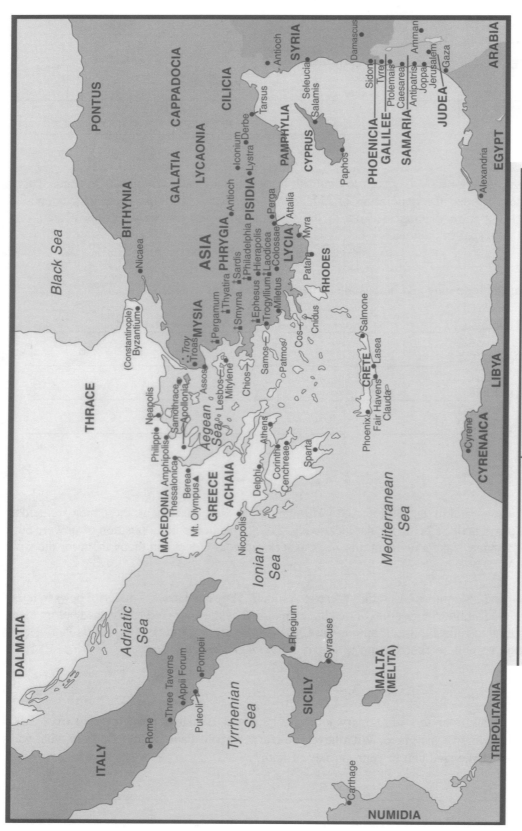

**Paul's Second Journey**

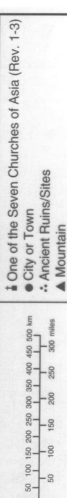

‡ One of the Seven Churches of Asia (Rev. 1-3)
● City or Town
∴ Ancient Ruins/Sites
▲ Mountain

# The Answer is Grace

Paul and Barnabas have returned from their first missionary journey. New churches have been planted all throughout the region of Galatia. Paul is refreshing himself in Antioch. This week we will look at an affliction that troubled Paul throughout his apostleship and travel to Jerusalem where the church of Jesus faces its most serious threat. We will also pack our bags and join Paul as he sets out once again on a journey to proclaim the grace of God.

## DAY 1

Throughout Paul's letters we find references to a "thorn in the flesh" which plagued him. While the references are vague, it is important to explore this piece of Paul's heart.

✔ Read II Corinthians 12:1-10.

Why is Paul given a "thorn in the flesh?" Who is the "thorn" from?

_____

_____

What request does Paul make of God regarding this "thorn?" How many times?

_____

What is God's answer?

_____

_____

● How do you respond when God says "no" to your deep, heart-felt requests? How should we respond? How do we learn to do this?

_____

_____

● What does Paul mean when he says, *"When I am weak, then I am strong?"* How do we develop this attitude?

_____

_____

Paul describes this event as having taken place *"fourteen years ago."* The writing of the book of II Corinthians is dated at 57 AD. Fourteen years ago then refers to the time Paul was in Tarsus after his departure from Jerusalem, around 43 AD.

Paul describes a man involved in a special revelation. There is little doubt that the man is Paul himself. He relates an experience in which he is brought to the *"third heaven."* Jews divided the heavens into three parts. The first is the blue sky we see on a sunny day. The second heaven is the realm of the stars and the moon — the vast reaches of space. The third heaven is the throne room of God.[1]

Paul, in this letter to the Corinthians, is defending the authority of his apostleship. False teachers have come into the congregation claiming that they have had revelations from God, thus making them superior to everyone else. Paul assures them that he too has had revelations, though he is not allowed to discuss them.

Seemingly as a direct result of these wonderful revelations, Satan is allowed to burden Paul with a thorn in the flesh. The reason God allows the affliction is to pierce Paul's pride. Remember, pride has always been a difficult thing for Paul to rein in. Since he was exceedingly proud of being a Pharisee, God does not want Paul to be overly proud of his ministry as an apostle. It is necessary for Paul to be constantly aware of the immense gulf his sin had created between God and himself and how the blood of Jesus fills that gulf. The purpose is not for Paul to drown in guilt, but to each day freshly feel the desire to share the good news of forgiveness through Jesus.

We are not told what form this thorn in the flesh took; however, many have guessed as to what it could be.

> The thorn has been speculatively identified as follows:
> Tertullian thought it was a headache.
> Klausner believed it was epilepsy.
> Ramsey identified it as recurrent malarial fever.
> Chrysostom said it was "all the adversaries of the Word."
> Calvin made it "fleshly temptation."
> Luther considered it "spiritual temptation."
> Knox decided it was "infirmities of the mind."
> Catholic commentators, generally, "lustful thoughts."
> McGarvey: "acute, disfiguring ophthalmia."
> Macknight spoke of some who believed it was "the false teachers."
> Lightfoot suggested "blasphemous thoughts of the devil."
> Alexander was sure it was "Malta fever."[2]

There is just not enough evidence from the Scriptures to conclusively say what form this thorn in the flesh took. Perhaps the Holy Spirit meant it that way. What is important about this affliction is not what it was, but the way Paul dealt with it. Three times Paul specifically went before the Father in prayer asking for the thorn from Satan to be removed. Each time God refuses to relieve Paul's pain.

> Being a Christian does not insulate us from the pain of life. Jesus never said He would remove our burdens. He promised to help us bear them.

What do Jesus' words in II Corinthians 12:9 mean to you? How will they help you bear your burden today?

_____

_____

When God refuses his request, Paul has two choices. He can walk away from God because He allowed the thorn to remain, or he can accept God's decision and live, through grace, in trust and acceptance. You have the same choice. Satan assaults us all. He attacks you in order to put a rift between you and your Father. Nothing defeats Satan more soundly than you standing solidly in the arms of Jesus. When his arrows fly, you have two choices. You can reject God because He allowed pain to enter your life, or you can hold His hand, revel in His grace, and triumph through trust and acceptance.

In Acts 15, the church established on the day of Pentecost comes to a crucial juncture. The pressure that has been building between the Jewish Christians and Gentile Christians explodes with the return of Paul to Antioch. This is the most serious challenge the church has faced and it is a question which we, as the body of Christ, still face today.

✔ Read Acts 15:1-2.

What are the men from Judea teaching? What do Paul and Barnabas do in response to this teaching?

_____

_____

Tension has been building among the followers of Jesus. On one hand, there are the believers that have the Jewish faith as their background. They believe in Jesus, but still practice all the requirements of the law — going to the temple, circumcision, ceremonial cleanness. On the other hand, there are a great number of believers who are pagan in their background. They know nothing of the Law of Moses, but rather had worshipped idols. By ancient custom, the Jews are not allowed to fellowship with anyone considered "unclean." This includes Gentile Christians since the definition of "being clean" involved circumcision and obedience to the Mosaic Law. The very fabric of unity between believers is being stretched and torn.

Paul comes into sharp conflict with those who are attempting to add to the simplicity of the gospel. He is uniquely qualified to address this problem. Having been a Pharisee, Paul understands, better than most, the requirements and the burdens of the Mosaic Law. He also understands the futility of trying to perfectly keep the law. God has shown him a more perfect way — Jesus Christ. Paul is not about to accept the burden of the law again.

What kinds of things do people try to add to the gospel message today?

_____

_____

# DAY 2

False teachers have begun to assault the church of Jesus claiming that all Christians must obey the Law of Moses in addition to submitting to the teachings of Jesus. Paul confronts these false teachers from Jerusalem. The church at Antioch sends Paul and a delegation to Jerusalem to put this question to rest forever. The central issue becomes "What is necessary for salvation?" Since Jesus was a Jew, is it necessary to go through Judaism to reach Jesus or did Jesus perfectly fulfill the Law of Moses, thus laying it aside and allowing all people to come directly to Him? This is no small question. The future of the church hangs in the balance.

✔ Read Acts 15:3-21 and Galatians 2:1-10.

How does Peter respond to the Judiazer's challenge?

_____

_____

What does Paul relate to the people?

_____

What truth does James bring to bear upon the question at hand?

_____

_____

Paul tells us that this trip to Jerusalem occurred fourteen years after his conversion. The date is 50 AD. The answer to the question that poured from the people's lips at Pentecost is being challenged. "What must I do to be saved?" Let's be very clear. The Holy Spirit has already decided the answer to that question. The only issue here is whether the church is going to follow God's direction or exercise its own will. The men here in Jerusalem did not decide what was necessary for salvation. Jesus did that on the cross.

✔ Read Galatians 1:8-9.

● What pressure does our world put upon us to change the gospel of Jesus? How must we stand up to this pressure? What should our prevailing attitude be when proclaiming the gospel of Christ?

_____

_____

Paul tells us that there were a series of private meetings that transpired prior to the public meeting recorded by Luke. The leaders of the church, the apostles, and elders gather to review the issue before them. This error threatens the very foundation of Christianity. Paul states in Galatians 2:2, that he went to Jerusalem in obedience to a revelation from the Holy Spirit. Paul went to Jerusalem to set the record straight. The matter is actually set to rest in these private meetings. Now the leadership goes before the congregation.

Peter recounts his encounter with Cornelius, recorded in Acts 10. He is made aware again that the cross of Jesus has torn down the barrier between people. He also recognizes the Jews' inability to keep the law. The law had not saved them, but the blood and grace of Jesus has.

Paul and Barnabas then recount their journeys to the Gentiles and the wondrous way they have received the grace of God. James, the brother of Jesus, then adds prophecy from the Old Testament as evidence of God's will.

● What tools do these men use to determine God's will?

_____

Peter, Paul, and James each base their judgment about God's truth on the direct, revealed word of God. Peter had four revelations from God concerning Cornelius. Paul received his command to go to the Gentiles from Jesus Himself. His ministry was confirmed through the Holy Spirit's demonstration of power. James quotes directly from the Old Testament. The truth is found in God's direct, revealed word.

 Read II Timothy 3:16-17 and II Peter 1:20-21.

● What is the direct revelation you have from God today?

_____

You hold God's truth in your hands. The Bible is the complete, revealed will of God. If we have a question about what God wants us to do, we need look no further than the inspired word of God.

The church at Jerusalem bends to the will of God. They announce their understanding that the path to Jesus does not need to go through Moses. His grace is a free gift to all of any nation who come to Him in faith and obedience. The issue of what is necessary for salvation is publicly laid to rest. Satan has come so close to destroying the unity of the believers, however, that he will continue to use these Judaizers as a weapon against the gospel. This battle will be something that plagues Paul for the rest of his ministry. Satan is still attacking the church in this way with this very question today.

● What are some ways that our world answers the question, "What must I do to be saved?"

_____

_____

In answer to Satan's pull, write Ephesians 4:4-6.

_____

_____

_____

The book of Galatians is written at this time in response to the questions raised at the Jerusalem conference. Judaizing teachers have already robbed the new Galatian churches of their joy by insisting that the law be upheld. Paul anxiously writes his children in the faith and encourages them to hold to the true teaching of Christ.

Galatians 3:23-25 summarizes the letter to the people of Galatia. Read these verses and record in your own words the theme of the book.

_____

_____

The assembled leaders then turn their attention to the question of how to bring unity to the body of Christ. Lifestyles differ so greatly between Jews and Gentiles that conflict still threatens to divide the church. The assembly agrees to ask the Gentiles, as a matter of courtesy and fellowship, to abstain from four things.

✔ Read the letter in Acts 15:22-35.

What four things do the apostles and elders ask the Gentile believers to avoid?

_____

_____

● Why would these four things hinder fellowship among the believers?

_____

_____

All four of these items – food sacrificed to idols, blood, strangled animals, and sexual immorality – are intimately related to the worship of false gods. Since Jews are taught from birth to avoid association with anything having to do with idols, the inclusion of any food at a common meal that has been tainted by idol worship is offensive. These guidelines are meant to ease the tensions between the different races as a matter of respect and brotherhood. Sexual immorality, of course, should be avoided altogether.

● What significance does the spirit of this letter have for us today?

_____

_____

---

♥ Respect and great love are to be the hallmark of the Christian community. Our personalities, lifestyles, and subtle prejudices must give way to Jesus' lordship as we strive to maintain unity within the body of Christ.

---

Our unity in Jesus Christ stands as a testimony to His love, grace, and power. When we stand united, we are able to lift His name before the world. When we fight among ourselves, we cannot glorify God. There is one Lord, one faith, one baptism. There is one answer to the question, "What must I do to be saved?" It is summed up in one word. Jesus.

# DAY 3

Since the moment Jesus appeared to Paul on the road to Damascus, he has been set apart to carry the name of Christ to the Gentiles. God uses Paul's personality, citizenship, commitment, intelligence, and loving heart to spread the good news of Jesus throughout the world. On his first missionary journey, Paul traveled with Barnabas to Cyprus and the region of Galatia. Now Paul is ready to set out again and for the love of Jesus, take the grace of God to Europe. Time has passed since the Jerusalem conference where Paul was instrumental in severing the cords that held Christianity to Judaism. Paul has been working diligently with the church in Antioch and is filled with a desire to revisit the churches he and Barnabas planted on their first trip.

✔ Read Acts 15:36-40.

What does Paul wish to do? Why?

_____

_____

What disagreement do Paul and Barnabas have?

_____

Who does Paul choose as a traveling companion?

_____

Here we see the tenderness in the heart of Paul. He remembers the faces of the new Christians and longs to give them strength and renew their commitment to the Lord.

An important lesson is found in this passage.

● What is our responsibility to new Christians?

_____

_____

Our commitment to new converts does not end in the waters of baptism. We see here from Paul's example that we must continue to serve and guide those we have led to faith. Christians do not grow in a vacuum. Like infants, they must be nourished not only by the Bread of Life, but by the touch of love from fellow Christians.

Barnabas agrees to a return visit but wants to bring along his cousin, John Mark. John Mark had previously accompanied them on their first trip, but deserted them midway through the journey.

The Holy Spirit speaks only the truth about the servants of God and shows us both the good and the ugly. Despite their eagerness to do God's work, the two brothers sharply disagree about John Mark. Barnabas wants to give John Mark another chance to do the work of the Lord. We can imagine that Barnabas reminds Paul during this disagreement how he was the only one who gave Paul a chance when he first came to Jerusalem after his conversion. Paul's heart on the other hand, is filled with his divine mission to take the gospel to the ends of the world. This requires traveling companions that he can count on with his life. John Mark, in his opinion, has proven himself unworthy.

The disagreement between the friends becomes so intense that they part company. As in the case of most arguments between friends, both parties are partially at fault. Both are strong-willed in their opinions and unyielding in their resolve. I'm thankful God shows us this incident. Paul is a real man, not perfect, just committed. God uses the situation, despite their failings, to further the gospel.

● What does this incident between Paul and Barnabas teach us?

_____

_____

Barnabas sets sail for Cyprus with John Mark. Although we will not see Barnabas again, we know from Paul's letters that his respect for Barnabas was great.

Paul chooses Silas as his traveling companion. With the blessing of the Antioch church, Paul and Silas set out on the second missionary journey.

It's time to get your map out. The journey that lies ahead is full of excitement and peril.

 Read Acts 15:41-16:5.

 *On the map located at the beginning of Lesson 5, mark the route taken by Paul in these verses.*

Where does Paul go? Who does Paul take with him on his second journey?

_____

Why does Paul circumcise Timothy?

_____

_____

● What lesson does Timothy's willingness to be circumcised teach you?

_____

_____

Paul sets out for the churches in Syria and Cilicia. There is much evidence that points to Paul as the catalyst for these churches during his quiet years in Tarsus. Now he returns to the land of his birth to strengthen and encourage the brothers and sisters there. From Cilicia, Paul and Silas travel through the mountain passes and return to Derbe and Lystra. It is here in Lystra that Paul once again encounters the young Timothy. He has matured into a wonderful Christian young man, well thought of by all the Christians in Lystra and Iconium.

✔ Read II Timothy 1:5.

Identify Timothy's mother and grandmother.

_____

> Never underestimate the impact of a mother's faith on her children! Because of the gentle faith of both Timothy's mother and grandmother, Paul finds a young man eager to accompany him on his mission of faith.

● What can you do to inspire faith in your children? In your grandchildren?

_____

_____

We are all aware of the importance of a mother imparting her faith, but I am so glad Paul includes Lois in his list of godly influences on the young Timothy. Grandparents are important people in the spiritual heritage of children.

Timothy has a unique heritage. While his mother and grandmother are Jews and have raised him with the stories of Abraham and Moses, his father is Greek. In order to streamline the spread of the gospel, Paul has Timothy circumcised. This means he can now travel and enter Jewish synagogues the world over without question. Paul did not circumcise Timothy as a prerequisite for salvation, but as a matter of expediency.

Read I Corinthians 9:19-22 and then write the last sentence of verse 22.

_____

_____

● Is this an attitude we should have today? In practical terms, how do we implement such an attitude?

_____

_____

So Timothy joins Paul and Silas as they proceed on their journey. They revisit all the congregations planted by Paul and Barnabas on their first trip, strengthening and increasing the family of God.

✔ Read Acts 16:6-10.

*Mark the route taken by Paul on the map located at the beginning of Lesson 5.*

Who stops Paul from going into Asia and Bithynia?

_____

● How do you respond when God opens a door for you? When He closes a door?

_____

_____

What vision does Paul receive?

_____

The apostle Paul is very sensitive to the leading of the Holy Spirit. He tests every move of the preaching team against the will of God. First, he tries to go south into Asia and its major city, Ephesus. This the Holy Spirit will not allow. So, the apostle proceeds to go north into the region of Bithynia and again the Holy Spirit will not permit it. Having come from the east and been blocked from going north and south, Paul sets out for Troas in the west.

● How do we learn to follow the leading of the Holy Spirit?

_____

_____

 May we, like Paul, lay every plan at the feet of Jesus.

In Troas, Paul has a dream. In this vision, a man from Macedonia, across the sea, begs Paul to come over. Paul immediately makes plans to leave for Europe.

We learn of an addition to the travelers in Troas. In verse 8, Luke refers to Paul and his companions as "they." In verse 10, the "they" becomes "we." Dr. Luke joins Paul in Troas and becomes an integral part of this missionary team.

## DAY 4

Paul is in Troas on his second missionary journey. Following a vision of a man from Macedonia begging them to come, Paul and his companions now set sail to take the gospel of grace to Europe.

 Read Acts 16:11-15.

 *On the map located at the beginning of Lesson 5, pencil in the path taken by Paul.*

To what major city does Paul go? Where does he find believers gathered?

_____

Who is the first European Christian? What is her nationality and trade?

_____

In Troas, Paul's traveling company sets sail for Macedonia. They dock at night on the island of Samothrace and proceed the next day for Neapolis, the port city for Philippi. Philippi was a Roman colony possessing the right of citizenship. The people of Philippi prided themselves so much on being Romans that they even dressed like the people of Rome. On the Sabbath day, Paul goes outside of the city to the river in search of worshippers of God. Evidently there is no Jewish presence in the city — a minimum of ten men were required to open a synagogue and not even that many could be found in Philippi. During the Babylonian captivity, the Jews had adopted the practice of meeting by places of open water for worship. See Psalm 137:1 In such a place, Paul finds a small group of women praying to Jehovah. What a strange sight for the apostle. Having been called into Macedonia by a vision of a man, the place he is to begin his ministry is comprised only of women. Much to Paul's credit, he does not doubt the leading of the Holy Spirit. He proceeds to teach the women about Jesus.

One of the women present is Lydia. A woman of Thyatira, Lydia sells cloth colored with the famous purple dye from her homeland. The dye was made from crushing the murex shellfish. The purple cloth is rare and valuable. Its expense makes it the garments of royalty.

Lydia responds to the message of Jesus and is baptized into His name. Not only is Lydia baptized, she guides her whole household to belief in the Son of God. This phrase "whole household" should be understood not to include small children and infants. Belief, understanding, and repentance are vital steps in the salvation process. These are the decisions of a mature heart and mind. Infant baptism is an erroneous teaching begun during the 3rd century AD.[3]

Along with the opening of her heart to God comes the opening of her home to Paul and his companions.

● In what way are Christianity and hospitality linked together? Why?

_____

_____

As Paul continues teaching the gospel in Philippi, an amazing series of events land Paul and Silas in jail.

✔ Read Acts 16:16-24.

Describe the girl encountered by Paul.

_____

● Why is Paul upset by the slave girl's proclamations? In what way are the girl's actions compromising the spread of the gospel? Compare Paul's reaction to that of Jesus in Mark 1:21-28.

_____

_____

● Are there people who compromise the spread of the gospel today? How should we respond?

_____

_____

What does Paul do?

_____

Why are the owners upset? What do they do?

_____

_____

What happens when Paul and Silas are brought before the courts?

_____

_____

In Philippi, Paul meets a girl possessed by an evil spirit. Through this spirit, she tells fortunes and makes a great deal of money for her owners. Yet, even the evil spirit knows Jesus. She follows Paul around shouting that he is a servant of the Most High God announcing the way of salvation. This is similar to the shouts of the spirit encountered by Jesus in Mark 5:7. Paul tries to ignore the situation knowing that it is ripe for trouble but, after several days, he casts the evil spirit out of the girl. The girl's actions are turning Paul's attempts to preach the gospel into a circus and disrupting the spread of the truth. The girl is focusing the attention of the people on the messenger, rather than the message. Paul cannot allow the message of Christ to be compromised.

When the slave girl's owners are hit in the wallet, they hit the roof. They may have been making a lot of money over the last few days as she created a sideshow by following Paul around. As with many people, they don't respond until their pocketbooks are in peril. They drag Paul and Silas before the city judges and stir up charges against them. A mob gathers and the magistrates order the men to be stripped and beaten. Paul and Silas are stripped and severely beaten with rods. Bloody and battered, they are taken to jail and fastened into stocks. The jailer is ordered to guard the prisoners carefully.

✔ Read Acts 16:25-34.

Describe Paul and Silas' behavior in prison. How are they able to act this way?

_____

_____

What does God send to save Paul?

_____

How does the jailer react to the earthquake?

_____

_____

Look at Paul and Silas. Their bodies are covered with bruises and blood. Their feet are locked in stocks. They are lying in the darkest part of the prison on the smelly dirt floor. Yet, amazingly, in the midst of their pain, Paul and Silas begin singing hymns and praying. Their bodies are in chains, but their spirits soar free. The other prisoners listen as their sweet songs rise above the prison's stench.

● Read I Thessalonians 5:18. How does the meaning of this verse change for you in light of Paul's imprisonment in Philippi? How is it possible to be thankful and praise God in horrible circumstances?

_____

_____

In response to His servant's situation, God sends a violent earthquake to the region. The jail doors spring open and the chains fall off all the prisoners. The jailer, in terror of the punishment that awaits him for letting his prisoners escape, prepares to kill himself. Paul stops him and the stunned jailer falls at the feet of the prisoners. In a moment of grace and irony, the man, who a few moments ago had felt free, now feels the chains of sin around his soul. Again we see the timeless question — "What must I do to be saved?" The jailer takes Paul and Silas and washes and tends to their wounds. He and his household hear Paul speak of the love and forgiveness of Jesus and, that night, they obey the gospel and are baptized into Jesus Christ.

What is the reaction of the jailer in verse 34?

_____

 Joy is the unmistakable mark of the presence of God. Only the grace of God can fill the soul with joy.

✔ Read Acts 16:35-40.

What happens when morning comes?

_____

Why does Paul refuse to go quietly?

_____

_____

Why are the officials afraid?

_____

The magistrates of the town have a change of heart, perhaps because of the earthquake, and order the release of Paul and Silas. They attempt to sweep the whole incident under the rug.

Paul, however, refuses to leave quietly. He identifies himself and Silas as Roman citizens. Under Roman law, the kind of punishment they have received is forbidden for Roman citizens. The officials are terrified. Their positions as Roman officials are in jeopardy if it is found out that they have violated the rights of Roman citizens. Giving in to Paul's demands, they escort Paul and Silas out of jail. It is important for Paul to make issue of their mistreatment by the authorities. In this way, he protects the new Christians to whom he is connected. It also gives validity to his message and provides public proof that he has abided by the local laws.

Before leaving Philippi, Paul returns to the home of Lydia. This must have taken some courage on Lydia's part to receive men who have incurred the anger of the city officials. It might affect her business interests. Despite the difficulties, Lydia opens her home to Paul and the believers in Philippi.

The believers at Philippi are especially precious to Paul. They become an oasis of love for him. They repeatedly provide monetary gifts for the apostle and the letter to the Philippians is a letter of love from Paul to these precious souls.

A church has now been planted on the shores of Europe. The word of God is spreading throughout the world. The love of one man for his Lord allows God to use him for His glory.

 God is still looking for people completely open to His will and His love. When we submit our lives to Him, He can use us to spread the love of Jesus throughout our world and thus bring Him glory.

● How can you more fully open your life to God's will?

_____

_____

1 Coffman, *II Corinthians,* p480
2 Ibid, p484-485
3 Shepherd, p59

# Noble Grace

Having been called into Europe by a man from Macedonia, Paul now leaves Philippi and continues on his missionary journey. This week his travels take him from hard-hearted Thessalonica to the nobility of Berea. Paul will also visit the wonder of Athens and the cosmopolitan Corinth. Get ready to travel. We have an exciting journey ahead of us this week!

## DAY 1

Paul and Silas leave the house of Lydia. Still sore from their beating, but rejoicing for the salvation of souls that took place, Paul and Silas set out for Thessalonica. They leave Luke and Timothy behind to strengthen and encourage the new Christians. Today Paul again faces persecution as he strives to take the grace of God to the world.

✔ Read Acts 17:1-9.

 *Mark the route Paul takes on the map located at the beginning of Lesson 5.*

To what city does Paul go? Where does he begin his preaching?

_____

At whose house is Paul staying? What happens to this man? Who causes this trouble?

_____

_____

What is the charge against Paul and his companions?

_____

Traveling on the famous Egnatia Way, Paul and Silas travel west about 100 miles to Thessalonica, the capital city of Macedonia. Isn't God's timing amazing?! The Romans have, throughout the Empire, constructed an excellent system of highways and roads for their armies. These arteries connect Rome with its vast empire. It also provides an excellent tool for the transmission of the gospel. Thessalonica is a free Roman city. It is a center for trade and travel. It has a large population of approximately 200,000, including a Jewish synagogue. It is here that Paul begins his teaching.

For three Sabbaths, Paul explains the central message of the Old Testament to the Jewish listeners — that Jesus is the promised Messiah. While Luke tells us of a small harvest of Jewish believers, he states that Paul's reception among the Gentiles is considerable. How long Paul stays in Thessalonica is unclear. It is evident from his letters to the Thessalonians that Paul stays longer than the three Sabbaths mentioned by Luke. Evidently after this period of teaching in the synagogue, Paul leaves the synagogue and preaches exclusively to the Gentiles of the city.

As in every location, Satan stirs up the Jews in Thessalonica against Paul. They become jealous of the response he gains from the town and the following he gathers for Jesus. Paul has been staying in the house of Jason in the city and the Jews incite a mob to rush the house. Unable to find Paul and Silas, they drag Jason and some of the other Christians before the local officials.

The charges they lodge against the teaching of Paul are very serious. The Emperor in Rome at this time is Claudius. He is very suspicious of the Jews and has, in fact, ordered all the Jews to leave Rome. The national pride of the Jews has resulted in rebellion around the Empire and the Emperor is intent on quashing the movement. Letters have even been sent forbidding Roman citizens from receiving these dissidents on their shores.

The Jews accuse Jason of harboring Paul, whom they claim is an enemy of Rome. They charge that Paul is proclaiming the kingship of another, this Jesus. This is considered treason of the highest sort.

The city governors require Jason and the others to post a bond. They are forced to put up money, perhaps their homes and businesses, as a guarantee that there will be no more disruption in the city. This places the apostle in a terrible position. For him to be silent is unthinkable, but to speak in this place means putting his new brothers in Christ in serious danger. Stopped by Satan from speaking the word, Paul leaves the city at nightfall.

● In what ways does Satan attempt to stop the spread of God's word today? How can we counter his attacks?

_____

_____

_____

Paul longs to return to Thessalonica. He feels his work there has been cut short and he aches to finish teaching the new Christians. Remember, they do not have the New Testament as a guide. They rely on the oral teachings of Paul to learn about their new Christian walk.

 Read I Thessalonians 2:17-18.

Who prevents Paul from returning to Thessalonica?

_____

Driven out of Thessalonica by the viciousness of Satan's attacks, Paul and Silas leave the main highway and journey about sixty miles to Berea. Here, in contrast to the hatred and close-mindedness found in Thessalonica, Paul encounters the refreshing spirit of the Bereans.

 Read Acts 17:10-15.

 *Mark Paul's footsteps on the map located at the beginning of Lesson 5.*

Where do Paul and Silas go?

_____

- Describe the character of the Bereans.

_____

_____

Who stirs up trouble in Berea? Where does Paul go?

_____

Open to the message that Paul is preaching about the Messiah, the Jews of the synagogue research the Law and the Prophets for themselves to examine Paul's claims. They are searching for truth and God brings truth to their door.

- How does the dictionary define "noble?" How does that description differ from God's definition of "noble character" in Acts 17:11? How would God describe your character?

_____

_____

_____

What an example to us all! With great eagerness, they receive the teaching about Jesus. They look forward to the next Bible lesson. Their hearts are hungry for the Bread of Life and their souls thirsty for the Living Water. The only way to grow in Christ is to feast on the riches of His word.

Thoughtfulness and maturity, however, accompany their eagerness. They take the time to examine the Scriptures themselves. They measure Paul's words against the word of God. This does not offend Paul; rather he rejoices in it. The Bible will always confirm the truth. We should consider this a warning and a responsibility. Any true teacher of God's word will find joy in you examining the Scriptures for yourself. If anyone asks you to lay your Bible aside and trust their word, run as fast as you can.

Finally, they examine the Scriptures *daily*. They do not wait a week for the next Sabbath, but search daily to discover the truth. We don't just feed our children on Sundays and expect them to grow strong and healthy. Kids need meals every day. (Mine seem to need five or six.) Likewise our souls cannot be expected to be spiritually healthy if only fed on Sunday. If we can find our way to the kitchen three times a day to feed our bodies (okay, maybe more than that) then surely we can find time to daily feed our souls.

● On a scale of 1 to 10, how is your Bible study like that of the Bereans? What do you need to do to improve in this area of your Christian walk?

_____

_____

As in Lystra, the Jews travel from neighboring Thessalonica when they hear of the success of Paul in Berea. They send delegates to the city to stir up trouble for the apostle. Can you see Paul shaking his head as he remembers who wrote the manual on pursuing Christians from city to city? Acts 9:1-2

Instead of staying and putting the saints in danger, the Berean brothers help Paul escape quickly from the city. To strengthen the new Christians, Silas and Timothy, who had rejoined him from Philippi, are left behind. The Bereans take Paul to the coast where he catches a ship. To their credit, the Berean Christians accompany Paul all the way to Athens to assure his safety. This gives us a glimpse of the love built up between Paul and the people who receive the grace of God from his lips.

● What promises do we have when it seems Satan is pressing in against us? John 16:33; I John 4:4

_____

_____

While in Athens, Paul is filled with fear and loneliness. He feels his spirit crushed by the evil of Satan. He has had to leave the last three cities under duress. He is worried about the new Christians. Are they facing persecution? Are they holding true to the name of Christ? Like a mother worried for young children left alone, Paul's spirit is burdened by his departure from his new brothers and sisters in Jesus.

Messages had been sent back with the Berean brothers for Silas and Timothy to join Paul in Athens. This indicates that Paul did not know where he was going when he left town. They probably caught the first boat leaving the harbor. While Luke does not record their arrival in Athens, the letter to the Thessalonians describes Paul's feelings.

✔ Read I Thessalonians 3:1-5.

Who does Paul send to the Thessalonians? Why?

_____

_____

What is happening to the Christians there?

_____

● Read Matthew 5:10-12. How are we to respond to persecution? What is your reward?

_____

_____

Evidently, persecution has befallen the church in Thessalonica. Paul, sick with worry and fear, anxiously longs to know about the brothers and sisters he left behind. Finally, he sends Timothy to check on them. At the same time, it has been supposed that Silas is sent to Philippi. For now Paul waits alone in Athens, filled with worry and dread about the souls so recently released from Satan's bondage.

# DAY 2

Forced from Thessalonica and Berea by the maliciousness of the Jews, a weary Paul settles in to wait for his traveling companions in the great city of Athens. Despite his frustration over the attacks Satan has mounted against him on his journey, Paul's heart cannot be silent for long. In a city where the great white marble temples gleam in the Grecian sun, philosophers argue in the market place, and magnificent works of art and sculpture grace the horizon, Paul stands on a hill and once again preaches the grace of God.

✔ Read Acts 17:16-21.

*On the map at the beginning of Lesson 5, mark Paul's journey to Athens.*

Describe the city of Athens. What catches Paul's attention in the city?

_____

● Like Athens, our society is religious but does not know God. Does this religious atmosphere help or hinder the spread of the gospel? Explain.

_____

_____

What does Paul do while he is waiting in the city? How do the people of Athens spend their time?

_____

● What similarities do you see between the Athenian way of life and our own?

_____

_____

What specific fact about the good news of Jesus catches the attention of the philosophers? Acts 17:18
Where do the Athenians invite Paul to speak?

_____

The magnificent city of Athens. Perhaps no other city has had as much impact on our modern western culture as this ancient Greek city. At the zenith of its influence and glory about 300 BC under the reign of Alexander the Great, Greece's impact on the world's art, literature, philosophy, medicine, and mathematics has been immeasurable. This is the culture that produced Plato and Socrates. From their structure of government, we drew the framework for our democracy.

When Paul walks the streets of Athens, however, it is not the incredible history and magnificent architecture that captures his attention. Paul looks straight at the soul of Athens and sees only emptiness and futility. The idols that dominate the city make Paul's heart burn with passion for the one, true God. Despite having been driven from the last three cities by threats and persecution, Paul cannot remain silent about the love and grace of God. As usual, he begins in the Athenian synagogue and takes the good news of Jesus to the Jews. Paul also takes his love for the Savior to the streets and speaks in the marketplace to the citizens of Athens.

While speaking in the marketplace, Paul encounters not only the common people, but the philosophers – the educated elite – of the day. Paul's teaching catches the attention of these local philosophers. He is teaching something new and different. Since they don't do anything but listen and discuss new ideas, they invite him to the Areopagus to continue his teaching. This is not a formal arrest or hearing. Out of curiosity, Paul is invited to speak. The Areopagus is a council that holds authority over matters of religion in Athens. Paul is asked to speak to this group on Mars Hill. If you go to Mars Hill in Athens today, there is a bronze plaque engraved with the full speech given by Paul on this occasion. In a sense, Paul is still preaching on Mars Hill.

✔ Read Paul's address to the Athenians in Acts 17:22-34. Read this passage slowly, out loud if possible. This is considered one of the greatest sermons ever preached. Take time to enjoy it and savor the truths it contains.

To what altar does Paul refer?

_____

● How is this audience different from Paul's previous audiences? What adjustment does he make? What lesson do you learn?

_____

_____

Paul approaches this group of people differently. He is not speaking to Jews who already believe in one God and are familiar with the Old Testament. He must start with more fundamental truths. All of these have their basis in Scripture, but there is no point in referring to something of which they have no knowledge.

● Next to each Athenian error listed below, write the truth about God that Paul relates to them on Mars Hill.

| The Athenian's Error | The Truth |
|---|---|
| There are many gods. | |
| The gods are unknown and unknowable. | |
| The gods dwell in temples made by man. | |
| The gods need to be served by man. | |
| Some people are superior to others. | |
| Each god is in charge of a piece of creation. | |
| The gods are remote and impersonal. | |
| Man's purpose in life is personal fulfillment. | |
| The gods are designed by man and made out of wood, stone, or metal. | |
| People's lives are determined by fate or chance. | |

● Which of these errors do you see as prevalent in our culture?

_____

Paul begins by commending the Athenians for their attention to the spiritual. He even refers to an altar he found honoring the "UNKNOWN GOD." So fearful of offending and upsetting the gods, they worship unknown gods just in case they had missed any. Thank God our confidence is not in what we don't know, but in Who we do know!

Paul begins by explaining that God's power and presence can be seen in the world He created. Much of what the Athenians worship is found in the natural world around them. Paul calls them to worship the Creator rather than the creations. He proclaims that God is the one, true God worthy of their worship.

As he looks around him from his vantage point on Mars Hill, Paul is struck at every view by temples designed to house idols. The Athenians are investing their souls in gods so small they can be contained in houses built by man. He tells the people that the God of heaven cannot be limited to a building. Paul no doubt remembers the words of Solomon, *"But will God really dwell on earth? The heavens, even the highest heavens, cannot contain you. How much less this temple I have built?"* I Kings 8:27 He tells them that God is infinite Spirit not bound by man's imagination.

Yet, while describing the eternal nature of God, Paul assures them that He is active in the activities of man. The Athenian's gods have to be begged to stop seeking their own pleasure and intervene in the affairs of men, or often these gods will interfere for their own mischief. Here Paul tells them that God is a personal, caring God. He loves His creation and sets each person in his place and time according to His will.

● What difference does it make to you to know that God has chosen for you to be in this place at this time? For what purpose has He put you here at this moment?

_____

The purpose of God's activity with man is so that man can know about Him. The Greek gods are shrouded in mystery. Their ways are confusing and unreliable. Paul tells the gatherers on Mars Hill that God's purpose for man is to seek and find Him. God is not hiding from us. He longs for us to reach out to know Him. When a heart searches for Him, it will find His presence close by.

Paul then uses the Greek's own poets to prove his point. God is so wise. God uses everything in Paul's background as resources for the spread of the gospel. His broad education is a valuable tool. Paul not only knows of their literature, but also their culture and religion. A native of Jerusalem would not have had exposure to Greek culture or insight to the Greek mind. God uses even Paul's place of birth as a tool for the gospel.

● In Athens, Paul uses things they are familiar with to teach them about God. What lesson do you learn from this? What in our culture today can you use to teach people about Jesus?

_____

_____

Paul reveals the coming judgment and the way of salvation. He calls the Athenians to leave behind their man-made idols and turn towards the one, true God. He tells them that God has confirmed these truths by raising Jesus from the dead. At the mention of the resurrection of the dead, the men of Athens start laughing at Paul. All the wisdom he has laid before them is nothing more to them than an interesting way to spend an afternoon.

● Have you ever been hesitant about talking about Jesus because you were afraid people would laugh at you? What does Paul's example teach you?

_____

_____

A few, however, respond to the call of Paul and turn to Jesus. We know of only two names, Dionysius and Damarius. A few others believe as well. One soul is precious to God and Paul cherishes the souls here that respond to the love of Jesus.

How does the response in Athens differ from the reactions Paul has received in other cities?

_____

Paul now turns his sights towards another Grecian city. As he stood on Mars Hill, Paul directed the eyes of the Athenians away from their idols and temples to another hill. That hill wasn't covered in marble or gold – just a cross. Stop now and thank Him that you do not serve an "unknown" God, but a God that longs for you to know Him and that, on that cross, showed you just how much He loves you.

# DAY 3

Today we travel with Paul as he leaves the apathy of Athens to preach in the sin-filled city of Corinth. I am thankful that God has allowed us such an intimate portrait of this wonderful man of God. We have watched as his zealous nature has been tempered with persecution. We have felt the rods hit his back as he bowed in service to Jesus. We understand so much more fully the attitude of a servant's heart having witnessed Paul's tireless service for his Lord. We have seen his love overflow into worry and fear for the young Christians he was forced to leave. We are strengthened as we observe Paul's courageous heart as he proclaimed the name of Jesus in the face of his accusers. And the story still has more chapters! I hope you have learned to love Paul through these weeks. God is still using him in a powerful way.

✔ Read Acts 18:1-11.

📜 *Trace Paul's route on the map located at the beginning of Lesson 5.*

Where does Paul go upon leaving Athens?

_____

Whom does he meet in Corinth? Why are they there? What is their occupation?

_____

_____

How does Paul support himself while in Corinth?

_____

In whose home does Paul preach the gospel? What is the response to the gospel in Corinth?

_____

_____

What does Jesus say to Paul? Why?

_____

_____

● When have you felt overwhelmed by the task God has laid out before you? What reassurances has He given you to help you complete your task?

_____

_____

How long does Paul stay in Corinth?

_____

Corinth is a unique and intriguing city. Located on the Isthmus of Corinth, the city is vibrant with trade and commerce. The Isthmus has two harbors, one on each side. Travelers dock at one harbor, place their goods on carts to transport them overland to the other harbor, and set sail for the far reaches of the world. This gives Corinth wealth, prestige, and a very cosmopolitan flavor. The region has at least twelve temples. Chief of these is the temple to Aphrodite. Located on the high mountain overlooking the city, the temple boasts 1,000 temple prostitutes. Sex with a temple prostitute equals worship to Aphrodite.

As a result of the vast wealth and large numbers of travelers, as well as the vile nature of the religious atmosphere of the city, Corinth is a morally depraved city. It is even considered immoral by pagan standards. The people of Corinth are always portrayed in the plays of the time as drunks. Even our English dictionary contains the word *corinthianize*, which means to act immorally. It is a city filled with every kind of evil. It is into this darkness that we see the apostle Paul bring the light of Jesus. He travels from Athens alone, still awaiting the arrival of Timothy and Silas with news of the believers in Thessalonica and Philippi. His heart is heavy with worry and loneliness as he approaches this great city of sin.

✔ Read I Corinthians 2:1-3.

How does Paul enter the city of Corinth? What is the focus of his heart?

_____

_____

● How can we make this the focus of our hearts?

_____

_____

Paul approaches Corinth in weakness, fear, and trembling. He knows well the limitations of his eloquence. The apathy of the Athenians surprises him. He has encountered vicious resistance to the word, but never total disregard. Perhaps here Paul has another battle with pride and self-sufficiency. He determines to focus completely on Jesus.

> With Jesus as the focus of our hearts, we are empowered to see His will, feel His strength, and be surrounded by His love.

Low on funds, Paul meets some Jews who are tent-makers. Priscilla and Aquila are refugees from Rome displaced by the edict of Claudius. Paul is invited to join them in their trade. Having this means of support, he proceeds to the synagogue to preach the message of Jesus. Weeks pass as Paul works during the week and preaches in the synagogue on the Sabbath. He brings his friends Priscilla and Aquila to the Lord and now has fellow workers both in the tent-making business and the faith.

Finally, Timothy and Silas arrive from Macedonia. They bring good news of the faithfulness of the new Christians as well as financial support for the apostle. The news is just the buoy that Paul needs. His spirit is refreshed by both the presence of Silas and Timothy and the news they bring. This brings to light an interesting note for us all. No Christian stands alone. We are interconnected in the body of Christ. Even the apostle Paul needs the sustaining power of friendship in the Lord. The church is designed by God as a place for us to join together to divide our sorrows and multiply our joys.

● Who has been a sustaining power in your Christian walk? How have they done that? For whom can you be a sustaining power?

_____

_____

In Corinth, Paul once again goes to the Jews first and once again the Jews reject the gospel. In protest, Paul shakes out his clothes as a symbol of his innocence with regard to their ultimate destruction. Paul is only responsible for the transmission of the gospel. The people who hear the message are responsible for their own response.

A Gentile named Titius Justus opens his home to the apostle as a platform for the preaching of the grace of God. Curiously, his house is next door to the synagogue. Everyday the Jewish leaders watch the crowd swell as Paul proclaims the love and forgiveness of Jesus Christ. Paul's teaching is so effective that even the leader of the synagogue and his household become believers. First Corinthians 1:14 tells us that Crispus is one of the few people baptized by Paul personally. In most situations, Paul preaches and Timothy or Silas baptize the people who make the decision to be saved by the blood of Jesus.

As the pressure between the Jewish leaders and Paul continues to grow, Paul receives a vision from Jesus. Filling him with courage, Paul is reassured by the presence of the Lord Himself and is encouraged to continue to speak with boldness. Jesus tells Paul that there are many souls that will be reached through his ministry.

● When do you most need a word of encouragement?

_____

The words of Jesus are similar to the words spoken by God to Elijah, the ancient prophet. At a time of extreme discouragement, God reassures Elijah that there are many faithful to Him. Perhaps Paul is weary in spirit as well. The constant pressure and tension of the pagan-dominated city, along with the abuse by the Jews, has to try Paul's heart. He must wonder if he can have any effect on a city so full of sin. Jesus tells Paul to stay true to his task and he will see a great harvest of souls.

With this encouragement from the Lord, Paul stays in Corinth a considerable time — eighteen months.

Paul spends the rest of his time in Corinth showing these pagan people the light of God. He also takes time to write two letters to the Thessalonians. In these letters, Paul tells the Christians at Thessalonica of his love for them and his desire that they continue to grow in their faith of Jesus. He also takes a moment to correct some misunderstandings that have arisen during his absence.

Persecution has surrounded the new Christians since Paul was forced to leave the region because of the Jews. His heart has been heavy since his departure. Timothy arrives in Corinth and brings encouraging news of their faithfulness. This sends the pen to the paper to tell of Paul's rejoicing.

Paul's letter gives the Thessalonians some very practical steps for Christian living. Remember, these people have come out of a background of paganism. The darkness of this life does not provide the people with a high code of moral standards. Paul needs to explain to them the basics of morality and holy living.

Scan I Thessalonians 4:1-12. Make a list of the instructions Paul gives them on living a holy life.

_____

_____

_____

● Which of Paul's instructions in I Thessalonians 4:1-12 is the most important to your Christian walk? Why? Why is being sanctified the key to understanding these instructions?

_____

_____

The main theme of both letters to the Thessalonians is found in Paul's address concerning the second coming of Jesus.

✔ Read I Thessalonians 4:13-5:11.

What are the two questions the Thessalonians have concerning the second coming?

_____

_____

What encouragement does Paul give concerning those who have died in the Lord?

_____

● How can we expect the arrival of Jesus when He comes again? What is to be our attitude while we wait?

_____

_____

Evidently the Thessalonians misunderstand Paul's teaching about the return of Jesus. They are concerned that those who died while waiting for Jesus will not be included in the second coming. Paul reassures them that those who die in the Lord hold equal hope with those who are alive. We can rejoice at the funerals of those we love in the Lord because we can be sure of their salvation and their resurrection with Jesus. This does not mean that we don't grieve for our loved ones. It means our grief is tempered with hope and faith. The Thessalonians also want to know specifically when the second coming will occur. Paul, echoing the words of Jesus, tells them that it will come like a thief in the night. Ours is not to know the day and time of His arrival. Ours is to live a life worthy of His coming at any moment.

● Do you live your life in anticipation of the Lord's arrival? Explain.

_____

_____

● What responsibilities does this passage place on us as we share the gospel?

_____

_____

The letter is sent to the Thessalonians. The Christians in Thessalonica, however, again misunderstand Paul's letter. Paul's reference to the suddenness of Christ's appearance cause many in that church to quit their jobs to await the Lord. They evidently saw in Paul's words that the moment of Jesus' coming is extremely imminent. Paul writes them a second letter to correct these misunderstandings. Today we know this letter as II Thessalonians. He encourages the Christians to work diligently and live lives worthy of the kingdom of God. Paul signs the letter in his own hand to assure the Thessalonians that the letter is authentic. The New Testament is slowly being written.

# DAY 4

After an extended stay, Paul decides that it is time to leave Corinth.

✔ Read Acts 18:18-22.

Who accompanies Paul on his journey?

_____

What happens in Cenchrea? Why?

_____

_____

What happens in Ephesus?

_____

_____

It has been a year and a half since Paul first stepped foot in Corinth and almost three years since he left Antioch. It is time to go home. The tears must have flowed as Paul left the Christians in Corinth who have become so dear to him.

Priscilla and Aquila accompany Paul as he begins his journey back to Syria. At the harbor of Cenchrea we have an unusual report. Paul gets a haircut! Paul cuts his hair in Cenchrea to signal completion of a vow he had taken some time earlier. Let's spend a few moments exploring the nature and focus of Paul's vow.

● What is a vow? Have you ever taken a vow? If so, briefly describe your vow.

_____

_____

Read Ecclesiastes 5:1-7. How does God view our vows?

_____

_____

Paul, as a former Pharisee, is familiar with a wide variety of vows that the Jews took as signs of special dedication or thanksgiving to God. While as a Christian Paul is under no obligation to participate in these vows, as part of his heritage he understands a vow's unique ability to focus the heart and mind on God. The vow Paul takes before the Lord is very similar to the Nazirite vow described in Numbers 6:1-21. While not specifically a Nazirite vow, I believe the special focus of this vow is the goal of Paul's heart.

✔ Read Numbers 6:1-8.

What is the focus of the Nazirite vow?

_____

Why would Paul make a vow like this at Corinth?

_____

_____

The vow Paul undertook is similar to a Nazirite vow. This type of vow could be taken by anyone, man or woman, who wanted to mark a special time of separation or consecration to the Lord. It was a time to completely focus on God. Remember Paul's resolve as he approached Corinth? This, I believe, is the impetus for the vow.

Write I Corinthians 2:2.

_____

_____

Corinth is a city completely drowning in its own filth. Paul is determined to keep his heart pure and focused on Jesus. He may have taken this vow as an instrument to constantly remind himself of the call of consecration he received from Jesus.

Define consecration. In what way have you been consecrated?

_____

_____

● How will the life of a Christian reflect its consecration to God? Ephesians 5:18; Galatians 5:16-25

_____

_____

_____

As Paul leaves Corinth, he cuts his hair as a sign of completing his vow.

● Why is our personal purity important to our Christian testimony?

_____

_____

● What do you do or avoid doing to maintain your purity?

_____

_____

_____

_____

Paul and his companions travel by ship and dock in Ephesus. Priscilla and Aquila decide to stay in Ephesus and make it their home. There Paul addresses the synagogue. Despite receiving a favorable response, Paul declines the Ephesians' invitation to stay. He is anxious to go home. He does promise, if the will of God allows it, that he will come back and visit with them. Remember at the beginning of this trip, the Spirit had forbidden Paul to go to Ephesus, sending him instead to Macedonia.

What lesson do Paul's words in Acts 18:21 hold for us?

_____

Paul sails for Syria, arriving at Caesarea. He makes a brief trip to greet the church in Jerusalem and then heads home for Antioch. Paul's second great missionary journey is at an end. It has been a trip filled with joy and hardship. Now Paul rests, but soon he will again pick up the cross of Christ and carry His name to the Gentiles.

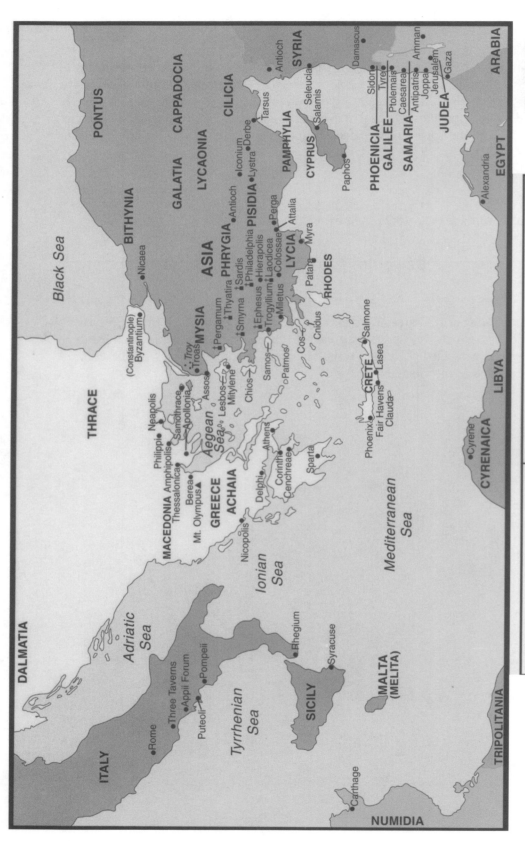

## Paul's Journeys A.D. 30-68

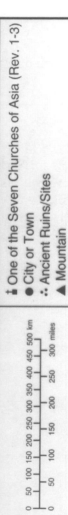

† One of the Seven Churches of Asia (Rev. 1-3)
● City or Town
∴ Ancient Ruins/Sites
▲ Mountain

| 0 | 50 | 100 | 150 | 200 | 250 | 300 | 350 | 400 | 450 | 500 km |
| 0 | 50 | 100 | 150 | 200 | 250 | 300 miles |

# The Power of Grace

This week we go with Paul to the great city of Ephesus. In this city filled with dark magic, God will shine the light of His grace and we will witness the incredible transforming power of the blood of Jesus Christ. As you travel with Paul this week, commit once again to living your life fully in His service. Thank Him for drenching your soul in the sweetness of His grace.

## DAY 1

Paul is at home in Antioch. This is the last time he will rest in the arms of fellowship with these Christians who are so dear to his heart. Today, Paul sets out on his third missionary journey and travels to the great city of Ephesus.

✔ Read Acts 18:23-28.

*Record the path of Paul on the map located at the beginning of Lesson 7.*

Which churches does Paul visit at the beginning of his third missionary journey?

_____

Describe Apollos. What is his error?

_____

_____

Who teaches Apollos? How do they teach him?

_____

_____

● Why does God give us such detailed information about the conversion of Apollos? What truth does He want us to see?

_____

_____

Where does Apollos go?  Acts 18:27

_____

We are not told how long Paul stays in Syrian Antioch. After refreshing himself in the company of his beloved friends, he once again tells them goodbye. Little does he realize that this will be the last time he sees this church family that helped to initiate his missionary journeys. He proceeds through the regions of Galatia and Phrygia revisiting the churches he established early in his missionary career. It is seems certain that he returns to Lystra, Derbe, Iconium, and Pisidian Antioch. Luke tells us nothing of his time in these places, only that the believers are strengthened by Paul's presence.

● Describe someone who strengthens you in the Lord. What are some practical ways for you to strengthen someone in the Lord?

_____

_____

While Paul is traveling in the region of Galatia, we are introduced to a man named Apollos, a Jew from Alexandria in Egypt. An eloquent speaker, Apollos travels to Ephesus proclaiming the message of John the Baptist. Luke is careful to tell us that Apollos is teaching very accurately the information that he has about Jesus and the baptism of John.

✔ Read Matthew 3:1-12 and review the ministry of John the Baptist.

John the Baptist had been sent by God to prepare the hearts of the people for the arrival of Jesus, the Messiah. He offered a baptism of repentance, meaning they could be baptized to show the beginning of their new life which was committed to preparing for the coming of the Messiah. This is the message that Apollos is teaching. He is still waiting for Jesus! In his audience in Ephesus we are again introduced to Paul's friends, Priscilla and Aquila. We must be impressed with the manner in which these two wonderful Christians teach Apollos. They quietly invite him into their home and explain about the life, death, and resurrection of Jesus. They do not ridicule him or publicly mock him. Instead, they gently guide him into a more mature understanding. It is a worthwhile conclusion that Aquila baptized Apollo and he becomes a powerful spokesman for the gospel of Christ.

● What lessons do you learn from the way Aquila and Priscilla handle this situation?

_____

_____

● How should we approach those in error? II Timothy 2:24-26

_____

_____

From Ephesus, Apollos moves to Corinth and is a mighty advocate for the word of God.

✔ Read Acts 19:1-7.

*On the map located at the beginning of Lesson 7, mark the route of Paul.*

Whom does Paul encounter when he first arrives at Ephesus? What does he ask them?

_____

_____

What do they do after Paul teaches them? Why?

_____

_____

What special gift does Paul give them? Why?  Hebrews 2:3-4

_____

_____

As Paul arrives in Ephesus, he meets twelve disciples. In their conversations with Paul, they tell him of their belief in the coming Messiah as preached by John the Baptist. Paul asks them a very pointed question, *"Did you receive the Holy Spirit?"*

The Holy Spirit, and His work in the lives of believers, is the identifying mark of a Christian. It is the very presence of God in the heart of the saved.

The fact that they have not heard of the Holy Spirit is unusual since John frequently spoke of the Spirit. These men were most certainly taught by Apollos before he himself learned of Jesus. Paul teaches them about Jesus. Beginning with the words of John, Paul explains that the Messiah has come to Israel, indeed the world. Hearing this good news, the twelve men are baptized into the name of Jesus and receive the precious gift of the Holy Spirit. Paul then lays his hands on the men and they receive a special filling of the Spirit. This is done to assure them that they now rest fully in love of Jesus. This kind of special filling of the Spirit is not necessary today. We have the word of God filled with promises and reassurances of our place in the Father's heart, the intercession of Jesus on our behalf, and the work of the Spirit in our lives.

● In what way is the gift of the Holy Spirit connected to our obedience to Jesus?

_____

_____

● How can you be sure that you have received the Holy Spirit?

_____

_____

# DAY 2

Paul has arrived in the great city of Ephesus. He settles into the city and begins to share the grace of God. Paul's time in Ephesus will bear much fruit for Jesus.

✔ Read Acts 19:8-12.

How long does Paul preach in the synagogue? What is the result?

_____

_____

Where does Paul continue his teachings? For how long?

_____

● What kind of miracles does Paul perform in Ephesus? Why do you think these miracles are necessary in this place?

_____

_____

Paul's ministry at Ephesus is extremely powerful and effective. He stays here for close to three years. Acts 20:31

Ephesus is the leading city in Asia Minor. It is a free city in the Roman Empire, maintaining its own government. It has an important harbor on the Aegean Sea as well as connections to the important trade routes of the time. Especially important in Ephesus is the temple to the goddess, Artemis. Corresponding to the Roman goddess Diana, Artemis is worshipped in a temple at Ephesus that is considered one of the seven wonders of the ancient world. The temple is 425 feet long and 220 feet wide with 127 columns. Coins from that era portray Artemis as a many-breasted fertility idol. Legend holds that her image fell from the sky at Ephesus. Many have speculated that perhaps the original image was a fallen meteor. Artemis is served by priests and priestesses and visited by travelers from all over the known world. Surrounding the temple, flourishing businesses have been established. Just like today, no one wanted to return from a trip to the great temple without a souvenir. Thus there is great demand for miniatures of the goddess made from a wide variety of materials. Also closely associated with the worship of Artemis are the black arts of the occult. Astrology, magic, sorcery, and demonism fill Ephesus.

● What areas of the occult are popular today?

_____

_____

● How does God feel about such practices? Why? Deuteronomy 18:9-13; Revelation 21:8

_____

_____

It is into this city that Paul goes to preach the gospel of Jesus. As is his custom, he begins at the synagogue. For three months, he pleads and argues with them about the present nature of the kingdom of God. No one can listen repeatedly to the gospel of Christ and remain indifferent. Either one's heart is softened by the love of Jesus or the heart is hardened as it refuses to bow before the Lord.

While there are certainly some Jews who are saved, the hardness of most drive Paul from the synagogue. They not only refuse to listen to the gospel, but also publicly abuse the name of Jesus. Paul leaves them, discouraged that his own countrymen will not listen.

As in Corinth, Paul finds another place from which to preach the grace of God. Tyrannus is master of a lecture hall and opens his doors to Paul for the spread of the gospel. Classes in these schools were generally held in the cool of the morning, dismissing around noon. Many agree that Paul used the time in the middle of the day, when school was not in session, to teach and encourage people to come to Jesus. The approach is extremely successful.

Write Acts 19:10.

_____

_____

From his base in Ephesus, Paul is able to send the word of God throughout the Roman province of Asia. Many of the seven churches we read about in Revelation probably owe their origin to the preaching of Paul in Ephesus. Because of the wickedness of the city and the special attention to black magic, Paul is given power by God to do extraordinary miracles. The sick are healed and demons cast out, not only by Paul himself, but also by pieces of cloth that had touched him. These handkerchiefs and aprons are the ones he uses in his tent-making business, which he resumed with Priscilla and Aquila. The sweaty, stained handkerchiefs are taken by people and placed on the ill, making them well. It is necessary to show the pagans in Ephesus that the name of Jesus is mighty and powerful. They need to see that Jesus is supreme over the power of the sorcerers of Artemis, whom they so ardently worship.[1]

✔ Read Acts 19:13-16.

What happens to the seven sons of Sceva?

_____

_____


Rather than resulting in belief, however, some try to use the name of Jesus like a magic spell. The seven sons of Sceva claim the power to cast out demons. They see that Paul has power that they do not and try to use the name of Jesus without committing themselves to it. The results are almost funny. The evil spirit, of course, knows the name of Jesus and even knows the name of His mighty servant, Paul. The evil demon, however, will not listen to the authority of these pretenders. He sends them running out of the house naked and bleeding.

● What do you learn about Jesus from the experience of Sceva's sons?

_____

_____


● How do people try to "invoke the name of Jesus" today? Explain the difference between using the name of Jesus and committing yourself to the name of Jesus.

_____

_____


The result of the unusual event surrounding the sons of Sceva is that the name of Jesus is held up all over Ephesus with great honor and respect. It is similar to the reaction of the people in Jerusalem after the death of Ananias and Sapphira. The message is clear: no one can use the name of Christ in trickery and pretense for his own advantage.

The other conclusion this event brings to people's minds is also significant. Christianity cannot just be thrown into a melting pot of beliefs.[2] Many people want to exercise some of the principles of Christian living without adhering to them all. This is completely unacceptable to God. You either worship Him only through His Son Jesus or you do not worship Him at all.

● In what ways are Christians tempted to water down the gospel and/or combine the truth with other beliefs?

_____

_____


✔ Acts 19:17-20.

What do the Ephesian believers burn? What are the books worth?

_____

In order to open the people's eyes to His love, God has allowed Paul to do great miracles in the name of Jesus. The extraordinary demonstration of God's power has captured the attention of the entire city.

Here in Ephesus there are many believers who have clung to their sinful ways while trying to follow the example of Jesus. They continue to practice magic and sorcery. This powerful demonstration of the supremacy of Christ pricks their hearts. They openly come forward and repent of their sins. They then burn expensive books of black magic in a public bonfire. Understand, there are not bookstores on every corner as there are today. Books are very rare and valuable. The value of the books is placed at 50,000 drachmas. To put the books' great value in perspective – the wage of a poor laborer was one drachma per day. An expensive fire indeed!

● The Ephesian Christians burned the magic scrolls to permanently separate themselves from their sin and to strengthen their commitment to Christ. Is there something you need to "burn" in your life to improve your relationship with God? Why are some sins so difficult to let go of? Why is it necessary to do so?

_____

_____

When Jesus washes away our sins in baptism, we are new creatures. As new creatures in Him, we must take hold of a new life and disentangle ourselves from the hold of sin.

Take a moment to thank Jesus for rescuing you from the clutches of sin. Ask Him to give you strength and power to say no to temptation. Cling to Him as you walk daily by His side. Feel the refreshment of forgiveness and grace fill your soul.

## DAY 3

While Paul is in Ephesus, he receives some disturbing reports about the conduct of the church at Corinth. A message has been sent from Chloe's household (I Corinthians 1:11), that divisions and sin fill the church at Corinth. Paul also receives a letter from the Corinthians asking for spiritual advice regarding a number of practical issues, such as marriage, food sacrificed to idols, and spiritual gifts. Paul writes the Corinthians a letter, which we know as I Corinthians. It is written in early 57 AD from Ephesus. While the first letter to the Corinthians covers a wide range of topics, it has two overriding themes. First is the absolute necessity for moral purity. The Corinthians, as you remember, come out of an extremely vile society. The Christians in Corinth are having difficulty letting go of the widespread immorality that plagues their city and adhering to the purity and holiness taught by Jesus.

✔ Read I Corinthians 6:13b-20.

Why does Paul say we should avoid sexual immorality?

_____

_____

● Name some of the immoral forces at work in our society. How do we, as Christians, counteract their influence in our homes? At work? At church?

_____

_____

_____

● In practical terms, how do we teach our children the importance of purity?

_____

_____

Corinth is not the only place saturated with sex. Our society is drowning in its own permissiveness. Music, movies, books, and television bombard us with the anything-goes sexual message. Maintaining the sexual boundaries of marriage is not just old-fashioned thinking — it is the command of God.

 Moral purity is to be a benchmark characteristic of the Christian community.

Our bodies are not ours, anymore than are our talents, time, money, or energy. They belong to God. As the place of Christian worship, our hearts should not be contaminated with sexual filth.

The second theme woven through this letter to the Corinthians is the unity of the body of Christ. The believers at Corinth have divided themselves into factions. They are suing each other in the courts. They show no respect for fellow believers during the Lord's Supper. They argue about who has the greatest spiritual gift.

Paul presents the Corinthians with an enduring picture of the make-up and function of the church.

✔ Read I Corinthians 12:12-27 and Ephesians 1:22-23.

Draw a picture of the church and label the parts.

- Explain why the physical body is a good representation of the spiritual body of Christ.

_____

_____

- Explain why the physical body is a good representation of the spiritual body of Christ.

_____

- What part of the body are you? In what ways are you interconnected to the rest of the body? What responsibilities and privileges does this give you?

_____

_____

_____

Paul gives us a beautiful and practical picture of the church as the body of Christ. Jesus is the head of the body. It is in Him and through Him that we have life. Just as your head guides your entire body, so Christ must lead the church. He gives it direction and purpose. As parts of the body, we are interconnected with Christ and each other in a unique way. We do not function independently. Rather, we join together to work for a common purpose. Feet cannot function without legs, eyes are protected by eyelids, each piece is nourished by the digestive system. Each blood cell is as important as the heart that pumps those cells for neither would work without the other. This interconnection provides us with special privileges. We are not alone. When we hurt, others know our pain. When we fall, others will help to pick us up. We stand united with the whole body of Christ. These privileges also lay a responsibility on our hearts. We are not alone. Our actions and purposes must be for the good of the whole body. Each part of the body has a function that must be fulfilled or the entire body will suffer. The lessons from this simple picture are endless. Perhaps one of the most important lessons is the value that God places on you and the price He paid to make you a part of His body – the church. Paul closes the letter to the Corinthians by telling them of his desire to come and see them. He then sends the letter with Timothy and Erastus as they go through Macedonia.

# DAY 4

Paul's efforts to spread the grace of God in Ephesus have been extremely successful. In the course of only two years the Holy Spirit tells us that *"all the Jews and Greeks that lived in the province of Asia heard the word of the Lord."* Acts 19:10 Amazing what God can do through the heart of one servant completely devoted to Him! Today we will watch as Paul begins to feel the Spirit's pull to leave Ephesus. Paul starts making travel plans so get your passport ready!

✔ Read Acts 19:21-22.

To what two cities does Paul specifically want to go?

_____

Where does he send Timothy and Erastus?

_____

One of the driving forces behind this third missionary journey is the collection of relief funds from the Gentile churches for the Christians in poverty in Jerusalem. At the Jerusalem conference, the only request Peter, James, and John made of Paul was that he remember the poor. Galatians 2:10 Paul has made requests among the churches he has visited to take up a collection for the poor in Jerusalem. After delivering the contribution to Jerusalem, Paul plans to go to Rome.

Read I Corinthians 16:1-4. What process does Paul set up for the collection of gifts by the believers?

_____

Today God calls His people to give as well. Giving a measure of our resources to God is a special blessing that requires self-discipline and sacrifice. God does not ask us to give because of His need. God asks us to give so that we might become more like Jesus – to learn the joy of trusting God's provision, the beauty of God's sacrificial love, and the delight that comes from giving God an expression of our praise. Jesus teaches us that our giving is not about the amount we give, but the heart with which we give. See Luke 21:1-4. It is our heart that He wishes to shape and giving is one of the tools with which He shapes it.

✔ Read II Corinthians 9:6-15.

● How are we to give to the Lord? Why?

_____

_____

● What will be the result of our heart-felt giving to God?

_____

_____

● Why is our giving a good barometer of our spiritual maturity?

_____

_____

✔ Read II Corinthians 8:1-7.

● What example do the Macedonians give us with regard to giving? In what way should we imitate their example?

_____

_____

● How do you grow in the grace of giving?

_____

Close to the conclusion of Paul's time in Ephesus, an unusual thing happens. Paul is not attacked by the Jews, but by the local businessmen of Ephesus.

✔ Read Acts 19:23-41.

What is the concern of the craftsmen?

_____

_____

Of what has Paul convinced a great number of people?

_____

● Examine Paul's influence on the business climate in Ephesus. What can you and your congregation do to have this kind of impact in your community?

_____

_____

What happens in the city?

_____

The Way has again disturbed the pocketbooks of the unsaved. As in Philippi, the businessmen begin to complain about their dwindling profits because of the teaching of Paul. In Ephesus, Paul has convinced so many people to turn away from idolatry that the market for the silver miniatures of Artemis has dried up. Imagine being so effective in your testimony for Christ that the local "sin" businesses start complaining! Demetrius and the other craftsmen believe that if Paul continues, Artemis herself will be robbed of her divinity. Of course, a god whose divinity can be taken away by men is not much of a god to begin with.

Who prevents Paul from going before the crowd? Why?

_____

What happens in the theater?

_____

_____

As has happened in so many other places, the craftsmen are able to stir up the crowd. The people of Ephesus have an unusually fanatical devotion to Artemis. As many as 25,000 people rush into the local theater. Luke tells us that in the confusion, many do not even know why they are there. Efforts are made to seize Paul, but, unable to find him, they grab two of his traveling companions, Gaius and Aristarchus.

What is the cry of the Ephesians?

_____

The Jews decide to seize the opportunity to condemn the members of The Way publicly and they push Alexander, a Jew, in front of the crowd. The Jews, however, have miscalculated the mood of the people. To the Ephesians, the Jews are just as bad as the Christians. Neither promotes worship at the temple of Artemis.

This sets off a great cry in the theater. For two hours the crowd shouts, *"Great is Artemis of the Ephesians!"*

Paul, bold for Christ as always, wants to go out before the crowd. Government officials discourage his going and the disciples keep him from entering the theater.

Finally, the city clerk is able to calm the crowd. He points out the openness of the courts, the grandness of the temple of Artemis, and the lack of evidence against Paul and the Christians. He then reminds them of the wrath of Rome. Their status as a free city is dependent on maintaining local order. A riot might ruin their position before the Emperor. The crowd goes home and Paul and the Ephesian church escape unharmed.

Ephesus has provided Paul with a unique platform from which to preach the grace of God. From it, the light of Jesus has been shown throughout the region. Christians abound in many cities and the church of Jesus Christ continues to grow. Paul, however, is not content. Tomorrow he continues on his journey for Jesus.

1 Tenney, p293
2 Ibid.

# Compelled by Grace

The people of Ephesus have spent an afternoon crying, "Great is Artemis of the Ephesians," but Paul's entire life testifies to the greatness of God. Paul leaves Ephesus and begins his journey to Jerusalem and eventually Rome. This week we catch a glimpse of the tenderness of Paul's heart and watch as a revelation of great trouble steels his resolve to completely walk by the grace of God.

## DAY 1

Paul has just completed his great work in the city of Ephesus. Having been there three years, he must say goodbye to dear friends. Paul feels the tug of the Spirit to proceed with his mission to the Gentiles. Today we will go with Paul as he revisits Macedonia and Greece and prepares to head for Jerusalem.

✔ Read Acts 20:1.

*Mark the steps taken by Paul on the map located at the beginning of Lesson 7.*

Where does Paul go?

_____

Paul heads north up the coast of Asia Minor and stops at the port city of Troas.

✔ Read II Corinthians 2:12-13.

Who is Paul waiting for in Troas? What is Paul's frame of mind?

_____

_____

● What do you do when you have *"no peace of mind"*?

_____

_____

The situation in Corinth is weighing heavily on Paul's heart and mind. Titus was evidently sent to Corinth to gather a report of how the Corinthians are behaving and how they received Paul's letter. While he preaches the good news of Jesus in Troas, his thoughts are filled with another place. When Titus doesn't meet him in Troas as expected, Paul is overwhelmed with worry about the Corinthian situation. He proceeds on to Macedonia, presumably to Philippi.

✔ Read II Corinthians 7:13-16.

What report does Titus give Paul concerning the Corinthians?

_____

_____

With great joy Paul receives the news that the Corinthians are being faithful to the teachings of Jesus. With this positive encouragement, Paul sends the Corinthians another letter, which we know as II Corinthians.

Second Corinthians is the most personal of Paul's letters. We learn more about his thoughts and feelings here than in any other letter.

Having been plagued with problems concerning unity and moral purity, the Corinthians are now beset by false teachers. These men are attacking the apostle Paul at every level. In response, Paul pours out his heart to the Corinthians. He reminds them of how he worked among them and of the example he laid out before them.

✔ Read II Corinthians 6:3-13.

What kind of example had Paul lived before the Corinthians?

_____

_____

● What kind of example should we live before our world? Why?

_____

_____

Most frustrating to Paul are the attacks on the authority of his apostleship. These false teachers are claiming to be "super-apostles" having advanced knowledge of God. Paul reminds them of the special miracles he performed among them confirming his mission from God. II Corinthians 12:11-12 Paul now recalls the great price he has paid to be an apostle of the gospel.

✔ Read II Corinthians 11:16-31.

Make a list of the things Paul endured for the cause of Christ.

_____

_____

_____

● Would you stay true to your calling if you had endured what Paul endured? What gave him the strength to endure all these hardships?

_____

_____

Look again at the list you made above. It's been a rough ride for God's servant.

Now in light of that list, write Philippians 3:8.

_____

_____

● How do we make Philippians 3:8 our own statement of faith?

_____

_____

Despite all the hardships that have pressed upon him, Paul considers them all worth it for the sheer joy of knowing Jesus Christ.

The presence of Jesus, the peace that comes with His forgiveness, the hope of eternal life with Him are worth more than anything on this earth.

As Paul closes the letter, he encourages the Corinthians to stay true to Jesus. He tells them of his plan to visit them and urges them to complete the collection of moneys for the poor in Jerusalem.

## DAY 2

From Philippi, Paul now sets out to visit the saints in Corinth. From this great city, he writes one of the masterpieces of the New Testament.

 Read Acts 20:2-3a.

*Mark the path of Paul on the map located at the beginning of Lesson 7.*

Where does Paul now travel? How long does he stay in Greece?

_____

_____

Paul leaves Philippi in Macedonia and heads for Greece. He spends the next three months in Corinth strengthening the church that has struggled so much. From Corinth, Paul writes another letter. This letter is different, however, because it is written to a church that he has never visited — the church in Rome.

The book of Romans is considered a masterpiece in its consideration of the fundamentals of the Christian faith. Paul writes the book to lay the groundwork for a future visit. The book of Romans is a treasure chest filled with many jewels of spiritual truth. We only have a moment to look at a few of the most priceless gems in the letter.

Paul spends a considerable amount of the first part of the letter exploring the condition of both Jews and Gentiles before the Father. His concludes that neither group is able stand before a holy God. The only solution, Paul explains, is found in the redemptive work of Jesus. In Jesus, both Jews and Gentiles find access to the blood of Jesus through faith and obedience.

Write Romans 3:22-24.

_____

_____

_____

● In what way do we fall short of God's glory?

_____

_____

Paul then explains the impact of the redemption we having so freely been given. He demonstrates that as we move from death in sin to life in Christ, we must identify ourselves with the Holy Spirit and seek the things of God. He explains that the Holy Spirit has been given to aid us and present our petitions before God. Then, in one of the most beautiful statements in the New Testament, we are assured of God's tremendous love for us.

● Read Romans 8:38-39. What is the extent of God's love for you?

_____

Take a moment to read that again. Do you really believe that? Have you responded to that love? That kind of love, His love, and our obedience to it, are what will carry you through the darkest nights of your life. It will help you soar with joy. It will wipe away your tears and give you peace. It expresses itself in the sunsets and butterflies. It carries our prayers to the heart of our Father, as surely as it carries our sin away from His face. It surrounds us, envelopes us, and holds us securely to the heart of God.

● What kinds of things make it difficult for you to realize God's great love for you?

_____

_____

Paul ends his letter to the Romans by telling them of his plans.

 Read Romans 15:23-33.

Where does Paul wish to go? Why?

_____

It has long been Paul's goal to visit Rome. He understands the influence of Rome on the world and knows that if Christ can be preached boldly in Rome, it will rapidly spread around the world. Paul makes plans to sail for Syria. He has collected a large contribution for the saints in Jerusalem.

 Read Acts 20:3-6.

 *On the map located at the beginning of Lesson 7, mark the route of Paul.*

What happens to Paul's travel plans? Where does Paul go instead?

_____

Where does Paul meet up with his traveling party?

_____

The Jews' hatred toward Paul has not abated. They make plans once again to take his life. Knowing how easy it would be to be trapped on a ship, Paul travels back to Philippi and makes arrangements to catch a ship there. Paul sends the men traveling with him on ahead to Troas. He spends a few days in Philippi. It is spring, the time of Passover. Then Paul, once again joined by Dr. Luke, sets sail for Troas. It takes five days to cross the Aegean Sea.

 Read Acts 20:7-12.

*109*

What day of the week does the church meet? Why do they come together?

_____

About how long is Paul's sermon?

_____

What happens to Eutychus?

_____

_____

● In what way is the story of Eutychus a spiritual warning to us as Christians?

_____

_____

Paul and his traveling companions meet again in Troas. They stay in the city for seven days enabling them to join the believers at Troas for their weekly worship together. The church gathers on Sunday for the purpose of breaking bread together. This is not a reference to the common meal, but to the Lord's Supper.

● Why does the church meet together on Sunday? Luke 24:1-8; Matthew 28:1-6

_____

> The participation of Christians in the Lord's Supper is the supreme reason we meet together weekly. We meet on the day of Christ's resurrection from the dead and remember Him in the Lord's Supper.

After the Lord's Supper, Paul speaks to the people. Knowing it will be a long time, if ever, before he will get to see these brethren again, he speaks until midnight. Talk about your long-winded sermons! While I know none of you has ever fallen asleep during a sermon, poor Eutychus does. Not only does he fall asleep, he falls out of a three-story window! At this Dr. Luke probably rushes outside with the crowd and pronounces the young man dead. Going downstairs, Paul lies down on the body and places his arms around the young man. Paul, through the power of God, raises the young man back to life. The whole congregation returns to the upstairs room. The people eat a meal together, offering further proof of the Eutychus' recovery, and stay to listen to Paul until daybreak. The raising of Eutychus provides us with not only a demonstration of God's love and power, but a vivid spiritual lesson. As Christians, it is so easy to become warm and complacent and tired from the day's work that, even in the presence of the word of God, we fall asleep, becoming inactive and unaware. Our hearts must remain focused on Jesus and our minds alert to the spiritual battle surrounding us.

Write Jesus' words to you in Mark 13:36–37.

_____

_____

# DAY 3

Paul sets out for Jerusalem as he completes his third missionary journey. This journey is difficult and exhausting, not so much because of the actual physical travel, but because of the Holy Spirit's warnings to Paul and the many goodbyes Paul has to say. Today we will watch Paul weep with dear friends and walk with determination and obedience toward the hardships that await him in Jerusalem.

✔ Read Acts 20:13-16.

*Record the journey of Paul on the map at the beginning of Lesson 7.*

How does Paul get to Assos? Why do you think he travels that way?

_____

_____

At what port does the group finally stop?

_____

When does Paul want to reach Jerusalem? How much time does he have?

_____

As Paul gets ready to leave Troas, he sends his companions on ahead in the boat. He decides that he would rather walk the twenty miles to the port of Assos. Why, after being up all night, would he wish to walk? I believe He wants to spend some quiet time with God.[1] We are going to see in a moment that Paul has received some disturbing news from the Holy Spirit about his treatment in Jerusalem. Paul needs time to be with his Lord. There will not be much opportunity for privacy on the ships and Paul seizes this moment for a walk with Jesus.

● How do you build quiet time with the Lord into your schedule? Why is it important?

_____

_____

I find it significant that Paul takes time to be with Jesus even though he is physically exhausted. Usually we want to wait until a convenient time – when we aren't tired, busy, stressed, or unhappy to spend time in God's word or in prayer. Yet this is exactly how Paul is feeling when he chooses to spend time with his Lord.

How much comfort, peace, and refreshment we squander by waiting for a convenient moment to approach our Father. Let us resolve to make spending time with Him a priority no matter what our schedule or mood. We may just find that our schedules aren't quite so stressful when we choose to take a walk with God.

This walk that Paul takes with Jesus is a picture of Paul's entire life and is an important picture for us. Every step of our lives must be taken holding the hand of Jesus. As we walk life's road, we may encounter bumpy trails, climb rocky mountains, and descend into dark valleys, but whatever the road, however the path twists, we can walk in peace and trust knowing He holds our hand and leads the way.

 Read Acts 20:17.

Who does Paul send for in Miletus?

_____

The boat that carries his friends picks up Paul in Assos and they sail to Miletus, stopping every night in a different port along the coast. Miletus is about thirty miles south of Ephesus. Not wanting to take the extra time to go into Ephesus itself, Paul asks the Ephesian elders to meet him in Miletus. Paul wants to be in Jerusalem by Pentecost. This gives him fifty days for the trip. Remember, he left Philippi right after Passover. He has already spent sixteen days in travel and does not wish to waste any more time.

 Read Acts 20:18-38.

Why does Paul want to see the Ephesian elders?

_____

● What does the Holy Spirit reveal to Paul? Why?

_____

_____

What directives does Paul give these men?

_____

● How can you apply Paul's directives to the Ephesians elders to your own life?

_____

How do the words of Jesus describe Paul's ministry in Ephesus?

_____

_____

● Looking at Acts 20:18-35, Paul describes his attitudes and actions while ministering in Ephesus. What kind of intensity do you see? Do you pour that much intensity into the ways you serve God?

_____

_____

How do they say goodbye?

_____

The people at Ephesus are very dear to the heart of the apostle. Here he had labored the longest. Here he has very deep ties. He calls the elders together to say farewell and give them important instructions about the care of the church.

He begins by recalling the time they spent together. He reminds them of his work among them, his tears for them, his courage in the face of persecution, his commitment to the preaching of Jesus.

He then tells them that the Holy Spirit has revealed to him that chains await him in Jerusalem. God is forewarning Paul about the hatred and persecution that he is going to face from the Jews. This knowledge gives Paul strength to face the days ahead. He knows God is in control of the world and holds him in His hand.

Write Acts 20:24.

_____

_____

 Paul's response fills me with awe. His only concern, his heart-felt desire, is to finish the task that God has laid out before him.

● What task has God given you to complete?

_____

_____

Paul also makes an impassioned statement about his innocence concerning the blood of men. While this statement seems odd, we must remember Paul's intimate knowledge of the Old Testament.

● What light does Ezekiel 3:17-19 shed on Paul's statement? What responsibility does this passage place on you?

_____

_____

As Paul tells the Ephesians good-bye, he exhorts them to tend to the church as a shepherd tends to his flock. He warns them of false teachers that will attack the church from within and without. He encourages them to hold fast to the love of Jesus Christ. Then this group of men kneels in prayer together. As the tears flow down their cheeks, love flows out of their hearts for this one who has given so much of himself to them.

# DAY 4

Luke keeps an interesting travel journal as they make their way to Jerusalem. He makes note of every port, but doesn't record any meetings with saints until the group reaches Tyre on the Phoenician coast.

✔ Read Acts 21:1-7.

*On the map at the beginning of Lesson 7, mark the path taken by Paul on his journey toward Jerusalem.*

How long does Paul stay in Tyre?

_____

What do the believers at Tyre say to Paul?

_____

● Why does Paul see the Spirit's warnings in a different light than other believers? What lesson does this teach you?

_____

_____

How do they say goodbye?

_____

The apostle Paul lands in Tyre and spends seven days with the followers of Jesus. Upon hearing of the sufferings about which the Holy Spirit has warned Paul, they urge him not to continue on his journey. Paul, however, is determined to follow the will of God. After kneeling on the beach to pray, Paul continues his journey.

✔ Read Acts 21:8-16.

📜 *Show the journey of Paul on the map at the beginning of Lesson 7.*

Where does Paul stay in Caesarea?

_____

Who comes to see Paul? What does he say?

_____

_____

What is the reaction of the people around Paul?

_____

What is Paul's reaction?

_____

_____

● Where in your life do you need to say *"The Lord's will be done"*? Acts 21:14

_____

When Paul arrives in Caesarea, he is welcomed into the home of Philip. Philip was one of the seven deacons chosen by Peter and the apostles to serve the needs of the Grecian widows. While at his home, the prophet Agabus comes to visit Paul. Many years earlier, Agabus had predicted a severe famine in the region. Now he comes bearing the prophecy of God for Paul.

In a dramatic moment, Agabus removes Paul's belt, a long piece of cloth, and wraps it around his hands and feet. He then announces that the owner of the belt will likewise be bound and handed over to the Gentiles. The room explodes with emotion as everyone pleads with Paul to refrain from going to Jerusalem. Many tears are shed as they express their love and fear for the one they have come to so admire.

For Paul, however, the message does nothing to change his resolve. He is ready to die in Jerusalem for the name of Jesus. Perhaps the face of Stephen once again flashes in his heart. He too is ready to make that sacrifice for the love of his Lord.

Paul finally arrives in Jerusalem. God has prepared him for what lies ahead. He has been told he would suffer many things for the sake of Jesus. His heart stands ready, his conviction sure. He stands in the arms of Jesus.

---

1 Coffman, *Acts,* p387

# Grace Rejected

After finishing his three-year stay in Ephesus, Paul has made a journey to Jerusalem. The trip has been filled with peril, heavy-hearted goodbyes, and warnings from the Spirit about the mistreatment Paul will have to endure. As he enters Jerusalem, Paul does so with a heart resolved to follow where Jesus leads. As you begin your lesson this week, take a minute to examine and strengthen your own resolve. Ask Him to fix your focus and commit yourself to taking each step today enveloped in the grace of God.

## DAY 1

Arriving in Jerusalem bearing the contribution of love sent by the Gentile churches, Paul is filled with mixed emotions. His excitement at seeing Jerusalem and his delight in bringing the gift are dimmed by the revelations he has received from the Holy Spirit. God has confirmed to Paul that the Jews will put him in chains and turn him over to the Romans. Today let's watch as Paul stands firmly for Christ in the face of those who hate him.

✔ Read Acts 21:17-26.

How do the brothers in Jerusalem greet Paul? What report does Paul give to the Jerusalem elders?

_____

What false report is being circulated about Paul?

_____

● Why, after the conclusions reached during the Jerusalem conference (Acts 15:1-30) is the law still such an issue in the Jerusalem church? What lesson do we learn from their struggle?

_____

_____

What do they ask Paul to do? Why?

_____

_____

● What lessons do you learn from Paul's acceptance of the vow? When is this kind of flexibility appropriate? Inappropriate?

_____

_____

_____

The brothers in Jerusalem receive Paul with joy. They gladly accept the gift of money from the representatives of the different regions of the Gentiles who accompanied Paul to Jerusalem. This, for Paul, is an answer to prayer. In Romans 15:30-31, he asked the Christians in Rome to pray for his reception in Jerusalem to be a positive one. The way in which he is greeted is a great relief to Paul. He proceeds to give them a detailed report about the work of God among the Gentiles. In less than a decade, Paul has taken the grace of God throughout most of the Roman Empire. On hearing of the multitudes of Gentiles who have believed the message of Jesus, they praise God. A shadow, however, still hangs over the church in Jerusalem. The problem, which brought Paul to Jerusalem eight years earlier, has, by this time, captured a majority of the Christians. The believers in Jerusalem are still zealously hanging onto the Law of Moses. They still consider Christianity an outgrowth of Judaism and participate in all the rituals and requirements of the law.

James and the rest of the elders in Jerusalem present Paul with a troubling dilemma. They know, of course, Paul's heart concerning the testimony of Jesus' fulfillment of the law and that a Christian's only restraint is obedience to the love and grace of Christ. They explain to him that the Jewish Christians are still zealous about the law. Adding oil to the murky water of this problem are false reports being circulated about Paul's teaching. It is being said that Paul is telling everyone to turn away from all that pertains to Moses and the law. They feel certain that his presence in Jerusalem will be a catalyst for great trouble if Paul does not show some sign of honor to the law. They ask Paul to sponsor four Jewish Christians involved in a temporary vow. They ask Paul to pay for their expenses and accompany them to the necessary sacrifices. Sponsoring this sort of action will be considered by all as a gesture of great generosity and charity and everyone will see that Paul does not despise the law.

This is a rather awkward situation and we can be thankful for the mature example we are given by Paul. Paul uniquely knows the value of the law in training and preparing the heart for Jesus. He also knows that Jesus has released all men from the requirements of the law and offers them the gift of grace. This gives a believer freedom in Christ. We have already learned from Paul that he is willing to become *"like a Jew, to win the Jews."* I Corinthians 9:20 Paul knows that the rituals of the temple do not make a person acceptable to God. Only the blood of Jesus can do that. Yet, he also knows that participating in this activity will not make him unacceptable to God either. While of no value to him personally, Paul is willing to accept this temporary burden to show the love and grace of our Lord.

Read Romans 14:1 and then write I Corinthians 10:32-11:1.

_____

_____

● How do these verses shed light on our relationships in the church?

_____

_____

✔ Read Acts 21:27-36.

Who sees Paul in the temple courts? Of what do they accuse Paul?

_____

● Read Ephesians 2:11-22 in light of Paul's experience here at the temple. What new light is shed on this passage because of the incident recorded in Acts 21:27-29?

_____

_____

● Under the law, there were boundaries in the temple preventing certain people from having access to the inner courts. What kind of boundaries do some set up that prevent certain people from having access to God?

_____

_____

What does the crowd do?

_____

_____

Who intervenes in the situation?

_____

Paul undertakes the act of goodwill recommended by the Jerusalem elders. As the week of purification is almost completed, Paul is seen in the temple courts. It is Pentecost and devout Jews from all over the world have come to Jerusalem for one of the three required feasts at the temple. Some Jews from Asia, probably from Ephesus, recognize Paul. What they could not accomplish in Asia, they see the opportunity to accomplish here. After seizing Paul, they begin shouting to the crowd in the temple. They accuse Paul of teaching against the Law of Moses and more specifically, of bringing a Gentile into the sacred Hebrew temple. This was something that was absolutely forbidden.

There is an outer court, called the Court of the Gentiles, into which foreigners are allowed. Boundary markers written in Aramaic and Greek warn of the penalty for passing into the holy temple area by Gentiles. The thought that someone so unclean had defiled their temple sends the crowd into a fury. They drag Paul out of the temple courts and begin to beat him. The gates of the temple are closed so as not to defile it by violence. The crowd is intent on killing Paul when the Roman guards disrupt them. Having a vantage point on the northwest corner of the temple in the Antonia Fortress, the Romans see the uproar and send guards to stop it. When the crowd sees the soldiers, they stop beating Paul. Assuming Paul has committed a crime, the Roman commander orders Paul chained. He asks the crowd for an explanation but they are so worked up, the commander understands nothing of what they are saying. In order to sort things out and calm the crowd, the commander orders Paul taken back to the Fortress for questioning. The violence of the mob is so intense that the soldiers have to carry Paul on their shoulders so that the crowd will not kill him.

# DAY 2

Paul has returned to Jerusalem with a gift for the poor from the churches throughout Asia. While in the temple, Paul is accused of defiling its holiness and is attacked by the crowd. The Roman guards in the city rescue Paul from certain death. As Paul waits in the Fortress Antonia to be questioned, he makes an amazing request.

✔ Read Acts 21:37-22:21.

In what way does Paul surprise the Roman commander? What unusual request does Paul make?

_____

_____

What does that request say to you about Paul? About God?

_____

_____

● Every other recorded time that Paul addresses a Jewish crowd he uses the Old Testament to show that Jesus is the promised Messiah. What different tactic does Paul use here? What have you learned about sharing the gospel from Paul?

_____

_____

_____

Paul takes the Roman commander, whose name is Claudius Lysias (Acts 23:26), by surprise. He speaks to him in Greek. Being in Jerusalem and arresting a man in the temple area, the commander assumed Paul only spoke Aramaic. He asks Paul if he is the Egyptian terrorist who had escaped Roman capture some time back. The Roman commander can think of no other reason for the vehemence of the Jews. Paul informs Claudius Lysias that he is a Jew, born in Cilicia. He then makes an unusual request. He asks to be allowed to speak to the people. Perhaps the request isn't so unusual for Paul, but the response is unusual. The Roman commander gives him permission. We have seen this in Paul before, but not so strikingly as we do here. Paul is a man of considerable presence and authority. His intelligence and calm manner convince the Roman to allow Paul to address the audience.

A few moments ago the crowd was so frenzied Paul had to be carried in order to escape their violence. Now quiet passes through the crowd. They give their attention to the one they were only minutes away from killing. Paul will not allow an opportunity to pass without speaking the name of Jesus. So precious is His love, so vast is His grace, that Paul feels compelled to share the gospel even with those who had just beat him. With blood soaking his skin and bruises swelling on his face, he turns to preach the good news of Jesus to the crowd.

 Nothing is more compelling than someone's personal story of salvation. A life changed, hope discovered, peace found.

Paul tells the crowd about his own conversion to Jesus. He dramatically emphasizes the divine nature of his call. He tells them of Jesus speaking to him, of the revelation of Ananias, and the vision in the temple they are standing before. All this the crowd listens to with expectation and openness. Paul, however, cannot reveal part of his call without explaining it all. He then explains the Lord's command that he will be sent to take this message to the Gentiles.

✔ Read Acts 22:22-29.

● What specific actions do the people take upon hearing of the Gentiles? Why? What lesson does that teach you?

_____

_____

Why does the commander order Paul flogged?

_____

What right does Paul invoke? What is the reaction of the soldiers?

_____

At the mention of the Gentiles, the hatred and fury of the crowd boils over. They begin shouting and throwing dirt in the air. As many are removing their cloaks, Paul surely must have seen in his mind's eye the cloaks that lay at his feet during the stoning of Stephen. The hatred on their faces reminds him of the hatred on his own that dreadful day.

✔ Read John 15:18-21.

● What kind of treatment does Jesus tell His followers to expect? Why?

_____

● How do you deal with the world's hatred?

_____

_____

The grief at the hardness of their hearts must have been overwhelming, not only to Paul, but to God. With the arrest of Paul, this is the last recorded time the gospel is preached publicly like this in Jerusalem. God was still holding out the message of forgiveness and reconciliation to the Jews. In 70 A.D., a few years from now, their zealously guarded temple will lie in ruins. God will judge the nation of Israel for rejecting its Messiah.

The Roman commander, Claudius Lysias, has no idea why the crowd reacts so violently to Paul. Unable to understand Aramaic, he assumes that Paul has committed some horrible act to which the crowd is responding. He orders Paul flogged. Flogging is not an ordinary beating. The victim is bound and stretched. The weapon — a series of whips tied together with little pieces of stone and bone attached to the ends — rips open the skin when it hits the person. Paul tells the soldier who is overseeing the preparations that he is a Roman citizen. This immediately sends alarm through the men. Roman citizenship guaranteed certain rights, among which was exemption from certain forms of extreme punishment, including flogging. The centurion reports Paul's claim of citizenship to the commander. Hurriedly, Claudius Lysias goes to Paul to verify the claim. Not only does he find out that he is a citizen of Rome, but that unlike himself who had to purchase his citizenship, Paul is a free-born citizen.

Write Philippians 3:20.

_____

_____

● How did you obtain this citizenship?

_____

_____

● What privileges and responsibilities does this citizenship give you?

_____

_____

Panic seizes the commander as he releases Paul from his chains. The violation of a Roman citizen's rights is a serious offense. Report of it could hold dire consequences for the commander.

Paul stays in the Fortress of Antonia as the Roman commander tries to sort out the charges against Paul. Tomorrow, Paul will again be called to give a defense of the gospel.

# DAY 3

As the Holy Spirit had forewarned, the Jews have bound Paul with chains. As he was worshipping in the temple, Jews from Asia seized him. This created a riot that almost resulted in Paul's death. The Roman commander in the Antonia Fortress broke up the furious mob and is now holding Paul prisoner.

Sore and bruised from the beating the Jews gave him the day before, Paul is called to answer before the Sanhedrin. Despite having saved his life twice, Claudius Lysias, the Roman commander, still does not know of what the Jews are accusing Paul.

✔ Read Acts 22:30-23:10.

What assembly does the commander call together?

_____

● In Acts 23:1, Paul says that he has fulfilled his duty to God in all good conscience. What is your duty to God? Are you fulfilling it? What do you need to begin doing today to be able to say that you have a "good conscience" about your duty to God?

_____

_____

_____

Why does Paul rebuke Ananias?

_____

_____

How does Paul divide the Sanhedrin? Why?

_____

_____

What is the commander once again called to do?

_____

The Roman commander calls the Sanhedrin, the Jewish ruling body, together. It is comprised of seventy men who have authority for all religious matters concerning the Jews. This is the same body who, almost thirty years before, had sentenced Jesus to die. The Roman commander places Paul before this group hoping that he will discover why there has been such a great disturbance. Paul stands before the Sanhedrin and looks them carefully in the eye. These are his countrymen. At one time in his life his ambition had been to sit in these chambers and with these men rule Israel. Now he looks at them and sees only spiritual blindness. Instead of leading the people to God, they killed the Messiah.

It is interesting that the first statement Paul makes to this body concerns the fulfillment of his duty and the innocence of his conscience. These men have neither fulfilled their duty to Israel nor live with a clean conscience. His comment outrages the high priest Ananias, who orders him struck on the mouth. Paul is stunned. Perhaps to this point he believed that he would have a fair hearing before the Sanhedrin. He knows that the law states you cannot hit a man who has not been found guilty. Paul uses the law, which they say he has violated, to show them that they are the ones who are guilty.

✔ Read Matthew 23:27-28.

Who spoke similar words? What does Paul mean by a "whitewashed wall?"

_____

_____

Paul has been away from Jerusalem for a long time and perhaps does not realize that he has spoken against the high priest. Several different men have held the office of the high priest during the last two decades and Paul may not know what Ananias looks like. He acknowledges the importance of respect for the rulers. Paul teaches us an important Christian principle in his apology to the high priest.

● Read the following and note (1) what authority is described and (2) what is to be our attitude toward them?

Romans 13:1-7, I Timothy 2:1-3, and Titus 3:1

_____

_____

_____

I Timothy 5:17 and I Thessalonians 5:12-13

_____

_____

_____

Matthew 28:18, Ephesians 1:19b-23, John 15:12, and John 14:23

_____

_____

_____

The incident with the high priest helps Paul decide on his best course of action. He now knows that the Sanhedrin will not listen fairly to his defense. He decides to seek support from the Pharisees in an attempt to separate the Sanhedrin along party lines. The best thing to do is divide and conquer. Paul announces to the group that he is a Pharisee, the son of a Pharisee. His family's commitment to the law has continued for generations. He then proclaims that he is being persecuted for his belief in the resurrection of the dead. This is entirely true. Since the moment Jesus appeared to him and changed the course of his life, he has been proclaiming the reality of the resurrected Jesus.

● In what way do you daily proclaim the reality of the resurrection?

_____

_____

These words ignite an age-old battle between the Pharisees and the Saducees. Some arguments can be rekindled with a single word. The Saducees are incensed. They claim there is no resurrection of the dead. The Pharisees side with Paul. Surely someone who believes in the resurrection of the dead is a good man. The argument escalates quickly. Things become so violent, in fact, that the Roman commander fears once again for Paul's life. He pulls him from the meeting place so that he will not get torn limb from limb. This is the third time in two days he has had to rescue Paul from the Jews.

# DAY 4

Paul returns to the barracks in the Fortress of Antonia. It seems understandable that the Roman commander does not know quite what to do. He cannot even get a straight answer out of the Jewish leaders. As night falls, Paul sits in prison waiting.

✔ Read Acts 23:11.

Who comes to visit Paul? Why?

_____

What does He tell Paul?

_____

Why is this important information for Paul?

_____

·What comfort does Jesus' visit with Paul give you?

_____

_____

Paul sits in the dark. He must be extremely discouraged as he waits in the prison cell. His future seems uncertain, his effectiveness diminished among the hard hearts of the Jews, his plans to go to Rome a distant dream. He is not even sure if he will live or die. In a precious moment, he is surrounded by Light. Jesus stands by his servant. He commends Paul for his witness of His name before the people of Jerusalem. He then tells Paul that he will be required to testify in Rome as well. What incredible comfort those words brought to the heart of Paul! Jesus gives rest to his servant's weary heart.

> In the same way, you can take courage in the presence of Jesus. He has promised to stand by you. He knows when you have been beaten by the world. He sees when the witness you give for Him is mocked. He watches as the forces of evil press in around you. Every moment of every day He stands by you.

Write the words of God to you in Hebrews 13:5b-6.

_____

_____

● Describe a moment when you were especially aware of Jesus standing by you.

_____

✔ Read Acts 23:12-22.

What is the plot of the Jews? Who is involved?

_____

● Who does God use to save Paul's life? What does God's use of a young person in this situation teach you?

_____

_____

Which two people does he tell? What caution does the commander give him?

_____

● How do you see the words of Jesus in Mark 13:9-13 at work in Paul's situation?

_____

_____

Evil begets evil and violence begets violence. The Jews hatch a plot to murder Paul. More than forty men join together in an oath not to eat or drink until Paul is dead. They then enjoin the leaders of the Sanhedrin in their scheme. The chief priests endorse the plan, even agreeing to lie to the Roman officials in order to get Paul out of the Fortress.

Paul's nephew becomes privy to the plot to kill his uncle. This is the first and only mention we have of the family of Paul. Whatever the relationship between Paul and his sister's family, his nephew warns Paul of the plot against his life. He goes to the prison and meets with Paul.

After hearing the evil conspiracy, Paul arranges for his nephew to tell the commander what he has learned. The commander seems unusually cooperative. Perhaps because he is still aware of his previous inattention to Paul's rights as a Roman citizen, the Roman listens to Paul's nephew. He warns the young man to remain silent and sends him home.

✔ Read Acts 23:23-35.

*On the map located at the beginning of Lesson 7, mark the route taken by Paul.*

What arrangements does the Roman commander make for Paul's transfer?

_____

_____

To whom is Paul sent? Where? When?

_____

_____

● Paul is sent out of Jerusalem surrounded by 470 soldiers. In this context, read II Kings 6:8-17. How might this picture apply to you today?

_____

_____

The Roman commander wastes no time making arrangements to remove Paul from Jerusalem. He orders 470 soldiers to make preparations to move Paul to the governor's palace in Caesarea, nearly sixty miles from Jerusalem.

As night falls providing darkness for their travel, the large contingent of armed Roman soldiers escorts Paul to Antipatris, about thirty miles north of Jerusalem. They carry with them a letter from the Roman commander, Claudius Lysias, to Felix, the governor of Judea. The letter informs Felix of the reason for Paul's transfer to the governor and the commander's conviction of Paul's innocence. He turns the whole matter over to the jurisdiction of Felix.

The group arrives at Antipatris without incident. Having left the threat behind in Jerusalem, the majority of the soldiers return to the Fortress of Antonia in Jerusalem. The seventy cavalry members escort Paul the rest of the way to Caesarea. Upon arrival at the palace, he is handed over to Felix and put under guard in Herod's palace.

Governor Felix reads the commander's letter and, after determining that jurisdiction is indeed his, commands that the trial of Paul will begin when the Jews accusing him arrive from Jerusalem.

It has been an eventful few days. Paul has been severely beaten and his life has been in danger four times. He has had the opportunity to speak the name of Jesus before all of Jerusalem as well as the Sanhedrin. Jesus is standing by Paul's side. I guess compared to that, the rest seems rather minor.

# In Defense of Grace

It has been twelve days since Paul's arrival in Jerusalem. He came to bring a contribution for the poor from the Gentile churches. Now he sits in prison. The Jews, having attacked him in the temple, have tried four times to kill him. Transferred to the governor's palace in Caesarea because of a death threat, Paul waits for his trial to begin.

## DAY 1

Paul is to appear before the Roman Procurator Felix. His full name is Marcus Antonius Felix. A freed slave, Felix has risen through the Roman ranks of government with his brother, who became a favorite of Emperor Claudius. Probably through that connection, Felix is named Procurator of Judea in 52 AD. Felix is not a man of high moral character although he is a crafty politician. He had some success putting down some rebellions in the region, including that of the Egyptian terrorist for whom Paul is mistaken. At the same time, he had the High Priest Jonathan murdered. The Roman historian Tactitus describes Felix in this manner, "In the practice of all kinds of lust and cruelty, he exercised the power of a king with the temper of a slave."[1] Felix's wife is a Jewess named Drusilla. This woman comes from a violent family. She is the daughter of Agrippa I, the man responsible for the death of the apostle James in Acts 12. Her great-uncle, Herod Antipas, killed John the Baptist and her great-grandfather, Herod the Great was responsible for killing all the infant boys under the age of two in an effort to kill Jesus. She is the sister of Agrippa II and Bernice. Historians record that she was an incredibly beautiful woman. Given in marriage at an early age by her brother, she left her husband, the king of Emesa, at the age of sixteen. Under the guidance of a magician named Atomos, she became the third wife of Felix. This is the man before whom Paul will give his defense.

✔ Read Acts 24:1-24.

Who comes to Caesarea to accuse Paul? What three accusations do they make against Paul?

_____

_____

How does Paul answer the charges against him?

_____

_____

How is it that Felix would be "well acquainted" with the Way?  Acts 24:24

_____

● Why is it not enough to be "well acquainted" with The Way?

_____

How does Felix rule in Paul's case?

_____

Five days have passed since Paul was transported in the night to Caesarea. Warned of a Jewish plot to murder Paul, the Roman commander in Jerusalem handed Paul's case over to the Roman Governor Felix.

The Jews arrive from Jerusalem in force. Even Ananias, the high priest, makes a personal journey for the trial. He perhaps feels that his presence will lend weight to the seriousness of the charges. The Jews bring with them a lawyer familiar with the practices of the Roman court. His name is Tertullus.

Tertullus opens the court proceedings. He begins by laying out the Jews' deference to Felix, showering him with flattery and compliments. He then levels three charges at Paul. First, he accuses Paul of being a mischief-maker upsetting Jews all over the empire. Second, he claims that Paul is teaching a religion not authorized by Rome. Third, Paul is accused of desecrating the sanctity of the Jewish temple.

The Jews in the courtroom express their agreement with the accusations and verbally verify their authenticity. It is most likely that as the Jews are attempting to persuade Felix to their side, they cannot hide their intense hatred for the one who had deserted their ranks. Paul is then given an opportunity by Felix to answer the charges.

Write I Peter 3:15.

_____

_____

● How do we prepare to give an answer?

_____

_____

● Why is establishing Him as Lord in our hearts an important part of this preparation?

_____

_____

● What kind of hope do you have?

_____

Paul begins by acknowledging Felix's tenure in the region. Acts 24:2 This is important because Felix has an understanding of Judaism and its belief system. He then answers the charges one by one.

First, Paul points out that he only arrived in Jerusalem twelve days ago. Five of those twelve days he has spent in prison in Caesarea! That is hardly enough time to instigate treason against Rome. He tells Felix that he in no way attempted to gather a crowd around himself. He had simply come to the temple to worship. Second, Paul answers the charges concerning teaching a new religion. He tells Felix that he is a follower of the Way and that the Way fully accepts the teachings of the Law and the Prophets. Christianity is the fulfillment of the Old Testament Law and Prophets. Everything God gave the Israelites foreshadows the Messiah. He did this to prepare them for the coming of Jesus. Paul also testifies about his belief in the resurrection of the dead. This has been a principle central to Judaism for centuries. It is not a new idea. Paul has dedicated his life to the preaching of the resurrection of one man, Jesus Christ. The principle foundation of Christianity is the resurrection of Jesus Christ from the dead. Everything else flows from our belief in that resurrection.

● Do you believe in the resurrection of Jesus Christ?

_____

If you said yes, then a change in your life is required. If you believe in the resurrection of Jesus, then obedience to that power is your only avenue. It is impossible to believe, truly believe, in the resurrection of Jesus and then do nothing. The power of that resurrection calls you to a new life, a new hope, a new beginning. It is a call to obedience. Once you obey Jesus through baptism, the power of the resurrection calls you to daily focus on your Lord. It calls you away from the things of the world to a new life focused in Jesus. The resurrection power is what transforms you into the image of Christ.

To the third charge of desecrating the temple, Paul tells Felix of the gift he brought to the poor. It demonstrates his love for the people of Israel. He specifically states that he was ceremonially clean as he stood in the temple that day. Paul then puts the icing on his defense. He asks where the witnesses are. The men who had originally accused him, the Jews of Asia, are nowhere to be found. The Sanhedrin itself could not bring a guilty verdict against Paul. He plainly tells Felix that there is no credible evidence against him. Felix decides to wait to make a verdict. He is well acquainted with The Way. He lives in Caesarea where Philip the evangelist resides. Members of his own Roman guard are members of The Way. Remember Cornelius? From his knowledge of The Way, he knows that the conflict between the Jews and Paul is not founded in Roman law, but in religious ones. He decides to wait until the more impartial Roman commander, Claudius Lysias, can be called from Jerusalem.

Felix orders Paul to remain in captivity, but grants him extensive freedom. He puts him under the charge of a centurion who is told to allow Paul some liberty and access to his friends and companions. Tradition holds that Paul was chained to this Roman guard with a long length of chain. The chain would be attached to Paul's right arm and the Roman's left. Most importantly, Paul's friends were allowed to see him. Roman prisons were not like our own. The state was not responsible for the care of prisoners. Those under arrest depended on those on the outside to provide them with food and other necessities. Paul, in being allowed to see his friends, was also allowed the blessing of fellowship.

## DAY 2

Yesterday, Paul gave his defense before the Roman governor Felix. While waiting for further witnesses to be brought from Jerusalem, Paul has an opportunity to share his faith with the man who will pass sentence on his case.

✔ Read Acts 24:24-27.

Who listens to Paul speak? What does Paul talk about?

_____

_____

● What is the reaction of Felix? Why is this such a dangerous response?

_____

_____

● What kinds of outside forces, like jobs or finances, work to keep people from Jesus? Why?

_____

_____

What does Felix really want from Paul? How long does Felix keep Paul in jail?

_____

● Why do you think God keeps Paul in confinement for two years in Caesarea? What lesson is He trying to teach Paul? Teach you?

_____

_____

This must have been a difficult time for Paul. He is not a man used to inactivity. Yet, even here God is working, molding Paul, maturing his faith. There is strong evidence that it is during this time that Luke gathers the information and research he uses to write his first letter to Theophilus. We know it today as the Gospel of Luke. Paul's experience here in Caesarea holds an important lesson for us. Sometimes God has us wait as well. Perhaps you are bound in a situation that you have prayed would changed, but it has not. God may be using this time to teach you patience and trust. He may also be using this time in your life for the benefit of others. Sometimes our waiting is not about us. Sometimes it is about other people with whom God wants us to connect, to share His love, to touch with His grace.

I have seen this truth worked out in my own life. For a long time my husband and I desired to move to another city to be closer to our family. God kept that door firmly closed. I went through a period of frustration as I tried to understand why God wanted us to stay where we were. Yet now, as I look back, I can see the faces of people who are now Christians because our lives intersected at this place. If I had not been there perhaps they would not have heard about God's grace. Of course, this intersection was not only for their benefit. My faith has grown and been strengthened as well – all because God wanted me to wait.

For the next two years, Paul is kept in prison under the authority of Felix. While understanding his innocence, the political situation demands placating the Jews. The scene that develops in front of Felix and Drusilla is one that is evidently repeated many times during those two years. Paul is called in to talk to Felix and his wife Drusilla. Paul spends this time talking to Felix about faith in Jesus. You can be sure that many times Paul preaches the gospel to this couple. Over and over he teaches them of the grace of God. He speaks to Felix on a wide variety of Christian subjects. They discuss righteousness, self-control, and judgment.

● What is righteousness? Why is it important? How do we obtain it?

_____

_____

Write II Corinthians 5:21.

_____

_____

● What is self-control? Why is it important? How do we obtain it?

_____

_____

Write Titus 2:11-12.

_____

_____

● Describe the judgment of God.

_____

_____

Write II Corinthians 5:10.

_____

_____

● Why does Paul choose to talk to Felix about righteousness, self-control, and judgment? How do these three things hold within them the message of the gospel?

_____

_____

The reaction of Felix to the preaching of Paul is noteworthy. He is afraid. If you are not in Christ, there is only fear. Paul explains how righteousness, the ability to stand before God, is found only in Jesus. We cannot obtain righteousness by ourselves. No matter how much good we do, no matter how much we give, no matter how we try, we are all sinners. There is nothing we can do to remove sin's stain from our souls. Sin separates us from God. There are no felonies and misdemeanors before God. There is no parole or probation. We are all guilty and are sentenced to death.

It is for this reason that Jesus died for you. He took your death sentence upon Himself. Because of that, we can cover ourselves in His righteousness and stand before God.

God has promised that judgment will come for everyone. On that day, God will ask you what decision you made. Did you accept the gift of Jesus and allow Him to pay the penalty for your sin or did you decide to pay that penalty yourself? You must make the decision about where you spend eternity today. Felix, however, does not respond in obedience to the gospel of Christ. He sends Paul away until a more convenient time. There will not be a more convenient time to commit your life to Christ. Satan will always provide an obstacle. He does not want you to go to Jesus.

● What kind of obstacles does Satan put in our path to keep us away from Jesus? How do they affect our relationship with Him?

_____

_____

Write the last sentence of II Corinthians 5:20.

_____

_____

Felix refuses to be reconciled to God and forces Paul to sit unjustly in prison for two years. The character of Felix comes shining through in Luke's note that he is hoping for a bribe from Paul. Felix waits for money while Paul offers him the riches of salvation.

# DAY 3

For two years Paul has sat in a Roman prison in Caesarea. He has presented the gospel to Governor Felix, but his heart is hard and unreceptive. Today a new governor comes to Judea and Paul is called again to give testimony about Jesus Christ.

✔ Read Acts 24:27-25:5.

Who is the new Roman Procurator?

_____

How quickly do the Jews bring their charges about Paul before the new Governor? What is the Jews' request?

_____

_____

Where does Festus convene the trial?

_____

In 59 AD, Felix is recalled to Rome for discipline. He has been unable to maintain peace in Caesarea between the Jews and the Gentiles. During one conflict between the two groups, Felix sends in soldiers who kill a large number of Jews.

His replacement is a man named Porcius Festus. Little is known of the background of Festus other than he dies in Judea two years later. Eager to establish good relations with the Jewish leadership, Festus makes a trip to Jerusalem. The change in leadership makes the Jews hopeful that they can once again lay hold of Paul. They ask Festus to allow Paul to come to Jerusalem for trial. The Jews have not given up their plan to murder the spokesman of Jesus. God's hand intervenes on Paul's behalf. The new governor orders the Jewish leaders to come to Caesarea for the new trial — their murderous plot foiled again.

✔ Read Acts 25:6-12.

Where does Festus want to move the trial? Why?

_____

Why does Paul refuse? What right of Roman citizenship does he invoke?

_____

_____

● Why does Paul invoke his Roman citizenship? Why doesn't he wait for God to supernaturally intervene in the situation and release him? What do you learn from Paul's example?

_____

_____

Festus soon reopens the trial against the apostle Paul. The Jews bring no new charges to the court and Luke passes over the accusations. Again they can produce no evidence to prove that he is guilty. Festus, however, cares less about justice than political gain. He sees Paul as a card he can play to gain favor with the difficult Jews. He asks Paul to go to Jerusalem and stand trial there.

Paul recognizes in this situation that he has no hope of ever being acquitted. He has already been locked in prison for two years on these false charges. Now there is a governor in charge who will give in to the wishes of the Jews for political gain. He knows that if he goes to Jerusalem they will kill him. Having no other choice, Paul appeals to Caesar.

The right of a Roman citizen to appeal his case to Caesar was very important. A slave or a conquered national received their ultimate judgment from the governor of the region. An Israelite, for instance, could go no higher than Festus. A Roman citizen, however, had the right to sidestep the often cruel judgments of the regional leaders and take his case to the courts of Rome. When a citizen invoked this right, the jurisdiction of the regional governor was curtailed. The only thing left for Festus to do was arrange transport to Rome.

Paul's appeal to Caesar will serve the purpose of not only saving his life, but advancing the spread of the gospel as well. When the highest court in the Empire declares Paul innocent, it will cloak Christianity with formal legal protection. The gospel can be freely spoken and none can hinder its spread. The acquittal of Paul before Caesar will bring down the last obstacles to the continued spread of God's word.

✔ Read Acts 25:13-22.

Who comes to visit Festus?

_____

What is Festus' dilemma? What does Festus conclude that the conflict between Paul and the Jews is about?

_____

_____

As a gesture of respect and courtesy, King Agrippa and his sister Bernice come to Caesarea. They wish to introduce themselves to the new Roman governor. During their stay, Festus tells Agrippa about the unusual case he has been left by Felix. Festus has figured out that the dispute is religious rather than civil and seeks Agrippa's advice. King Agrippa, being from the area, would have a greater understanding of the particulars of the Jewish faith. Agrippa has probably heard much about The Way and its followers. His family has been intertwined with the development of Christianity since the birth of Jesus. Agrippa welcomes the opportunity to hear the case.

✔ Read Acts 25:23-27.

The next day, Agrippa and Bernice enter the audience room with great pomp. The word *pomp* in the Greek indicates a vain and showy display.

Using what details we are given in Acts 25:23 and your imagination, describe the setting of Paul's encounter with King Agrippa.

_____

_____

_____

Into this atmosphere of luxury and self-indulgence the prisoner Paul is brought in. Despite the numbers of important people gathered, Luke focuses our attention on the two main players — Agrippa and Paul. Agrippa is a king, surrounded by every luxury. Paul is a prisoner, dressed simply and in chains. Yet who is true royalty? Agrippa, the king, is a prisoner of sin. Paul, the accused criminal, is the representative of the King of Kings.

Festus first addresses the crowd explaining his dilemma. Paul is being sent to Rome, but Festus does not understand his crime. He can find no wrong and yet the Jews are insisting on Paul's death. All he has figured out is that the dispute centers around a dead man named Jesus that Paul insists is alive. He pleads with Agrippa to help him unravel the case so that he can write the indictment for Rome.

● What prophecy is being fulfilled this day in Paul's life? Acts 9:15 In what way does remembering this prophecy help Paul as he stands before Agrippa? In what way has God worked in your the past to prepare you to face the difficult moments of today?

_____

_____

_____

# DAY 4

Today Paul stands before kings and rulers and gives an impassioned defense of his belief and life in Jesus. It is a powerful thing to stand up and tell others of the way in which Jesus has worked in your life. As we stand beside Paul, think about all the ways that God has worked in your life.

✔ Read Acts 26:1-23, if possible, out loud.

What does Paul tell Agrippa about the reason he is a prisoner? What "hope" is Paul talking about?

_____

_____

Write a modern-day translation of Jesus' phrase, *"It is hard for you to kick against the goads."*

_____

_____

● What two responsibilities did Jesus give Paul in Acts 26:16? In what way has Jesus given you those same responsibilities? In what ways do you see that you are fulfilling these responsibilities?

_____

_____

_____

Despite the physical appearance of Paul amidst all the splendor, he electrifies the room. His passion for Jesus finds voice in his appeal to Agrippa. Jesus told Paul that one day he would be called to speak before kings and rulers. Today is that day.

This is the third time the story of Paul's conversion has been recounted. It was the defining moment in the life of Paul. Jesus touched the heart of Paul on that road to Damascus and that heart now beats with love for his Savior.

Recall the moment of your conversion.

_____

_____

_____

Paul divides his defense into three main points. The actual sermon must have been considerably longer. Luke gives us a summary.

First, Paul impresses on Agrippa his background as a Pharisee and devout Jew. He tells the king that even his accusers can testify to his life as a Pharisee and his zealousness for the law. The men accusing Paul are not strangers to him — they are the men he grew up with and called his friends.

Paul then tells Agrippa, that quite ironically, it is the very thing he learned as a child — the foundational hope of the Jews — that is being held against him. He tells him that he is a prisoner because of the hope of the twelve tribes of Israel — the promised Messiah.

Second, Paul describes in detail the experience of his conversion. He recalls the way in which he tortured and killed the children of God. Many times he punished them and tried to force them to blaspheme. It must have been with a sense of both inner horror and the peace of blessed forgiveness that he tells Agrippa his tale. He then tells in colorful detail the divine vision he received. Paul relates the words of Jesus that left such an indelible mark on his soul.

On the road to Damascus, Paul was a young, proud, powerful, arrogant man and Jesus' statement about *"kicking against the goads"* is an expression describing Saul's stubborn resistance to the message of God's grace. Today we might say, "You are banging your head against a brick wall." I think perhaps as he looked at the king, Paul saw a reflection of the man he used to be in Agrippa's eyes. Paul aimed Jesus' words straight toward the heart of the stubborn young king.

Next he tells Agrippa of the two lifetime roles that Jesus gave him. Jesus appointed Paul to be both a servant and witness. Here is so beautifully described the life of a Christian. First, we are called to be servants of God. As we name Him Master of our hearts and lives, we allow ourselves to be used to His glory and for His purposes. Second, but perhaps of greater importance, Jesus calls us to be witnesses for Him. What does a witness in a trial do? They are required by oath to tell the truth — to explain what they have seen and heard. That is exactly what Jesus calls you and I to do each day. Our actions, words, activities, relationships, conversations, priorities — our lives — are to give testimony to the grace of God. The world will make its judgment about Christianity based on the testimony of His witnesses.

● What responsibility does this place on your heart?

_____

_____

Paul is a powerful witness for God. Jesus had commanded His apostles to begin in Jerusalem and take the gospel to the world. More than anyone else, Paul has done this.

● Outline the steps in a person's spiritual walk as described in Acts 26:18.

_____

_____

_____

Finally, Paul explains how Jesus is the fulfillment of the Law and the Prophets. Agrippa is fully versed in the prophets and Paul explains how Jesus is the one his people have been looking forward to for centuries. He tells him that Moses foretold Jesus' coming and his cruel death and glorious resurrection are simply the completion of the prophets' words. This message is the light of hope to both the Jews and the Gentiles.

✔ Read Acts 26:24-32.

What is the reaction of Festus to the gospel?

_____

What question does Paul ask Agrippa? Why?

_____

_____

What is Agrippa's response? What does this mean?

_____

_____

As the grace of God unfolds we are told of two reactions. We see in this room two different kinds of unbelievers.

The first is Festus. Festus interrupts Paul and accuses him of being a madman. He doesn't have any idea what Paul is discussing. In fact, he is embarrassed that he has even allowed Paul to speak. Festus is the man who, because of the depth of his depravity, has no interest in even trying to understand the message of God. God has given him over to the consequences of his sin. Festus is like the hard soil in Jesus' parable in Matthew 13. The seed never has a chance to germinate.

Write I Corinthians 1:18.

_____

_____

The second is Agrippa. Paul asks Agrippa pointedly if he believes in the prophets. Remember, Paul has just explained how Jesus is the Messiah and the fulfillment of the prophets. If Agrippa says "yes", he agrees with Paul and must then acknowledge Jesus as the Messiah. If he says "no" and denies the prophets, he risks angering the Jews. Agrippa is the man, who seeing the truth, turns around and walks away. Agrippa is like the rich, young ruler in Matthew 19. (In fact, he is a rich, young ruler.) This man, when presented with the opportunity to follow Jesus, turns around and walks away.

Write Matthew 16:26.

_____

_____

● How can procrastination endanger your relationship with God? Other people?

_____

_____

Agrippa and Felix reject the message of Jesus. They walk out of the reception chamber and out of the arms of God. Paul may be the one in chains, but these two men are the prisoners. Agrippa, however, is convinced of Paul's innocence with regard to any wrongdoing. The fact that Paul had to appeal to Caesar in order to save his life earlier now ties Agrippa's hands. Festus begins to make arrangements for Paul's transfer to Rome.

> Don't let the word "almost" come between you and God. Commit yourself fully to Him. Don't delay. Someday "almost" won't be good enough.

---

1 Conybeare, p602

# Grace Amid the Storms

We have an exciting journey ahead of us today. After two years in a Caesarean prison, Paul is put on a ship to Rome. Luke's account of the sea voyage of Paul and his traveling companions is told with the detail of an eyewitness. Put on your life jacket and get aboard. It is a good day for sailing. Bon voyage!

## DAY 1

Paul has appealed to Caesar. Festus is required to arrange transport to Rome. The voyage that follows is so beautifully told to us by Luke and is unique in two ways. First, it gives us an opportunity to glimpse the personality and heart of the apostle Paul. Second, Luke's account of the sea voyage is "one of the most instructive documents for the knowledge of ancient seamanship."[1]

✔ Read Acts 27:1-5.

📜 *On the map located at the beginning of Lesson 7, mark the route taken by Paul.*

Who is in charge of the voyage?

_____

What ship do they take? Who accompanies Paul?

_____

How does the captain of the voyage treat Paul? Why is this unusual?

_____

_____

In what two ports does the ship stop?

_____

It is the late summer or early fall of the year 60 AD. Festus finally makes the arrangements for Paul to go to Rome to stand before Caesar. He places Paul under the guard of a centurion named Julius of the Imperial Regiment.

Understand that there are no passenger ships in this time. All persons wishing to travel by ship, even the Roman Emperor himself, arrange transport on a cargo ship. This is the circumstance we find here. Paul is loaded onto a transport ship out of Adramyttium, a seaport in Mysia. Luke and Aristarchus join Paul on his journey. Also on board are a number of other prisoners bound for Rome. Most of these are destined for the cruel sports that take place in the theaters in Rome. Very few have the luxury of Roman citizenship like Paul.

Their first stop is in the port of Sidon, seventy miles up the Phoenician coast. Here the centurion grants Paul an unusual favor. He allows Paul to go ashore and meet with friends. From the very beginning, the centurion shows Paul respect and, as we will see, even deference. There is an authoritative presence about Paul that commands respect and draws people's attention. Coupled with that authority, however, is tenderness and profound concern for the eternal condition of people's souls. Rarely do you find the two so beautifully bound together. Paul meets with the Christians in Sidon and they provide for his needs. Once again we see the beautiful spirit of generosity that is prevalent among the early Christians.

The ship puts out to sea from Sidon. The most direct route across this part of the sea would be to go south of the island of Cyprus. Luke tells us, however, that the winds are so unfavorable that they are forced to go to the north of Cyprus, staying close to the coast. Sailing in this direction they travel past Cilicia. As they past that region, Paul can see the city of his youth. After many days travel, Paul's ship reaches the port of Myra in Lycia. Myra was an important harbor in the commercial travel of the Roman Empire. Corn and wheat were regularly transported by ship from the fertile Nile region in Egypt to Rome. Myra became an important stop on that sea-going trade route.

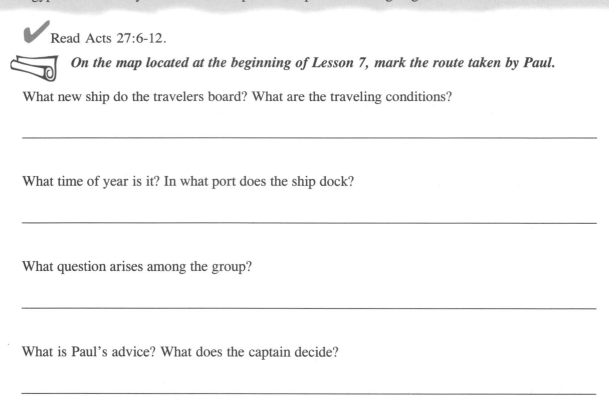

Read Acts 27:6-12.

*On the map located at the beginning of Lesson 7, mark the route taken by Paul.*

What new ship do the travelers board? What are the traveling conditions?

_____

What time of year is it? In what port does the ship dock?

_____

What question arises among the group?

_____

What is Paul's advice? What does the captain decide?

_____

_____

● To whom do you go to for advice when faced with a difficult decision? Why?

_____

_____

In Myra, the centurion finds another ship in port. It is a ship from Alexandria in Egypt. The ship is loaded with grain bound for Rome. The centurion takes the opportunity for a more direct voyage to Rome and loads the passengers onto the new ship. The weather on the Mediterranean is making it extremely difficult to travel. Luke tells us the time of year by telling us it is *"after the Fast."* The Fast to which Luke is referring is the Jewish Day of Atonement. It falls in late September/early October. The common rule of thumb holds that sailing on the Mediterranean is safe from May to September. The Romans consider sailing on the Mediterranean after mid-September dangerous. The crew tries to make the port of Cnidus on the coast of Asia Minor. When the winds do not allow their approach to Cnidus, they sail south of the island of Crete. The term to the "lee" of the island means that the island provided some protection from the wind. After a great deal of difficulty, the Alexandrian ship puts in at the harbor of Fair Haven on the southern coast of Crete.

● What difficult winds of life are you sailing through right now?

_____

_____

At Fair Haven, the crew of the ship discusses where to spend the winter. The winter months on the Mediterranean are too dangerous for sea travel. Traditionally, ships find a safe port and spend the winter months on land. In the spring, they can resume their trip. It is quite interesting that Paul is included in the discussion of what to do for the winter. He is being shown a great deal of courtesy, unexpected toward a prisoner of Rome. Paul advises, from his own experience as a seasoned traveler, that they should winter in the town of Lasea about five miles from Fair Haven. Laesa, however, is not much of a town and the pilot and owner of the ship prevail upon the centurion to proceed to Phoenix. Phoenix is a major city about thirty-six miles away that serves as a major winter port because of its naturally protected harbor. The majority of the passengers agree that they should sail for Phoenix.

What other "voices" offer you advice on how to sail the sea of life?

_____

_____

# DAY 2

Paul is on his way to Rome. It is, however, quite late in the year to be sailing on the seas and the crew on Paul's ship is looking for a port in which to winter. Having rejected Paul's advice, the ship and its passengers set sail and encounter a violent storm.

✔ Read Acts 27:13-26.

In what kind of weather does the ship set sail? What develops shortly after they leave port? Describe the storm.

_____

_____


Who visits Paul on the ship? What is the message?

_____

_____


The journey from Fair Haven to Phoenix can easily be made in a day with the right wind. When the crew notes a gentle wind come up, they think they have perfect sailing weather. It isn't long before the big storm hits.

The "northeaster" as Luke calls it, is the common name used by sailors. The official name is the Euroquilo. It is a hurricane-like storm with enormous waves and severe winds that rage off Europe from the northeast. The ship has no choice but to give in to the wind and drift with the waves.

While this is a very large ship, we should remember that it is made of wood. Made by hand, it is subject to great leaks and the wind and waves put stress on the wooden beams. It has one large mast rigged with one large sail. It has a double rudder system in the stern, or back, of the boat. On board is also a smaller boat used to take persons and cargo from the ship to the land in a harbor.

The storm threatens to overtake the ship. The whipping winds drive them past the small island of Cauda. These few moments respite from the terrible winds give the crew a chance to bring the small boat on board. In their confidence in sailing to Phoenix, they had allowed the smaller boat to be dragged behind the ship, anticipating its use upon their arrival. With the hard rain and the high waves the smaller boat was filling with water. With great difficulty, they manage to salvage it.

While some of the crew are busy with the lifeboat, others are passing ropes under the ship. This is a common practice in ancient sea travel. Luke uses a medical term to describe the procedure. He says they are "bandaging" the boat. This is a good picture of what they are doing. Ships carried with them large ropes that they pass crosswise under the ship to strengthen it. The waves put great stress on the wooden planks. Today, the naval term for this procedure is frapping.

● With what do you "bandage" your boat during the storms of life?

_____

_____

The third precaution the crew takes is to lower the anchor. The anchor is located on the bow, or front, of the ship. Dragging in the water, it acts to stabilize and slow the ship. The storm rages for days. Violent wind and rain tear at the ship. It is surely leaking in places and, as water threatens to further weigh down the ship, they begin to throw nonessential items overboard. This serves to lighten the ship as water is coming in, thus keeping the boat afloat. The storm is so intense that the sun and stars are completely out of sight. Modern ships, with compasses, radars, and sonar, are able to affix their position even in the most violent storm. Ancient ships, however, have none of these. It is so dark that they cannot even use the stars to figure out where they are.

● What kinds of things do people use to "fix their position" in life? What do you use?

_____

_____

As the storm shows no sign of abating and water pours into the boat, the people on board give up hope. They realize it is just a matter of time until they sink and perish. During the storm, Paul has been talking to God. God has assured Paul that he will go to Rome. An angel appears to Paul and gives him some encouraging news. Imagine the scene if you will. Paul gathers the tired, hungry men around him. The storm is raging. The rain is pounding the deck and the sound of the wind screams in your ear. The faces around you are filled with exhaustion and hopelessness. Paul reminds the men of his advice at Fair Haven. It underscores the truth of his message now. He tells them of a visit from an angel and how God has promised Paul that he and all the men with him will be safe. They will be shipwrecked on an island, but their lives will not be lost.

Write Paul's words in Acts 27:23.

_____

_____

Aren't those beautiful words? Paul describes himself using the terms _"whose I am and whom I serve."_

We do not only serve God, we belong to God. We are His children. In any situation we encounter, God wants us to remember, not only who we are, but also whose we are. When we understand whose we are, it changes our whole outlook on the situation.

Paul understands that he belongs to the One who calmed the sea. Not only should we remember whose we are, we should realize whom we serve. We are God's representatives on earth. You may not know my dad, but if you spend time with me, you will see what he is like. In the same way, those who do not know God get their first information about God from the changed lives of His children. Paul's faith in God gives the men on the ship hope. Isn't that the job of a Christian?

● What kind of confidence does Paul have? Acts 27:25 How do we develop that kind of faith and trust?

_____

_____

✔ Read Acts 27:27-44.

How long has the storm been raging? What new panic arises at midnight?

_____

_____

What does Paul encourage the men to do?

_____

What happens to the ship? How many men are on board? How many die in the shipwreck?

_____

● Why does God allow Paul to go through this experience of the storm and shipwreck? Why doesn't He just calm the sea? What question does this answer in your own life?

_____

_____

The storm rages for fourteen days. Imagine fourteen days of constant wind, rain, and waves. The ship is filling with water. You cannot stop the leaks. The pressure and the stress are becoming evident on the faces of the men. The ship has been so blown off course, no one has any idea where you are. Then you hear it. Waves crashing against the land. The experienced ears of the sailors hear the sound amid the tumult of the storm. This at once brings hope and panic. With land approaching, it might be possible not to go down with the ship. On the other hand, if the ship is sent crashing into the rocks, everyone will be lost.

The sailors quickly measure the depth of the water. They find the water to be 120 feet deep. A short time later, they again lower the weighted rope. They discover they are moving closer to land because the water now is only 90 feet deep. In a last ditch attempt to slow down the boat, they remove the anchors from the bow and throw them off the ship's stern. Hopefully this will provide drag on the boat and reduce its speed. The men then begin to pray for daylight so that they can see the approaching shore. Amazing how prayer becomes a viable option for those in danger. Some sailors, however, panic. They try to leave the boat using the lifeboat. They do not believe Paul's message that none will be lost. Paul sees their plan and informs the centurion. The centurion orders the lifeboat cut loose. Many people, like the sailors, think that they can save their own lives. They grab "lifeboats" and try to sail to shore.

● What are some of the "lifeboats" the world offers?

_____

_____

Paul tells the centurion that staying with the ship is the only guarantee of life. This is what God has promised. The men have to obey God's word in order to have life. There is no other way.

As dawn approaches, Paul once again addresses the men. He encourages them to eat as a matter of survival. The storm has been so violent and the stress so great that no one has eaten for fourteen days. In a beautiful moment, Paul takes the bread and gives thanks to God before all 276 men. His faith and sincerity give the men hope and they nourish their exhausted bodies. They then toss the remaining cargo of grain overboard so that they can go as far inland as possible.

At last a beach is spotted. The sailors cut the anchors that have been dragging behind the ship and lower the rudders and hoist the sail. They plan to drive the ship into the sandy beach. The boat, however, hits a sandbar as it approaches the island. The bow is so firmly stuck in the sand that it causes the waves to tear apart the rear of the ship.

The soldiers decide that the best course of action is to kill the prisoners. A Roman soldier had to substitute his life for that of an escaped prisoner. Because the prisoners might swim and escape, the soldiers plan to kill the prisoners and leave them on board the sinking ship.

The centurion, however, has a special affection for one prisoner — Paul. Not wanting his life taken, the centurion orders that none of the prisoners be killed. He orders those who can swim to set out for shore. The rest grab planks and debris and float into the beach. One way or the other, everyone makes it safely to shore. God keeps His promise.

God will keep His promises to you as well. No matter what the storm, no matter how dark the night, God will rescue you if you will let Him be Captain. He has not promised we will escape the storms of life, just that He will guide your ship and bring you safely home.

# DAY 3

Paul is on his way to Rome. In the midst of the voyage, the ship is ravaged by a severe storm. For fourteen days, the waves and the wind toss the passengers. Finally, the battered crew and ship approach an island. As the surf rips the ship apart, the 276 passengers make it safely to shore. Now we will watch as Paul arrives safely in Rome and Luke concludes his letter to Theophilus.

✔ Read Acts 28:1-6.

*On the map located at the beginning of Lesson 7, mark the route taken by Paul.*

Upon what island do the men land safely? What happens to Paul?

_____

_____

How do the people react?

_____

Exhausted and wet, the shipwrecked men land on the beach of Malta. In fact, the bay into which Paul swims is today known as St. Paul's Bay. All 276 passengers survive as God said they would. The natives of the island show the survivors unusual kindness. It is cold and raining and the islanders begin by building a fire to warm the soaking men. As he is putting wood onto the fire, a poisonous viper attaches itself to the apostle's hand. The reaction of the crowd is one of horror and resignation. The native inhabitants of the island recognize the snake. They have seen its terrible effects on their own loved ones. Understanding the painful death soon to strike, the superstitious natives apply pagan justice to the situation. Knowing Paul is a prisoner, they assume that the gods are resuming their attack on him. After failing to kill him in the shipwreck, the gods strike him with a snake. They watch and wait for the poison to take effect.

What promise did Jesus give the apostles in Mark 16:15-18?

_____

Paul does not die. He shakes the snake off his hand into the fire and proceeds with his activities. The people are stunned. Never has anyone escaped death after being bitten by such a snake. After watching him closely and seeing no ill effects, they assume he must be a god. While the content of Luke's letter is brief on this point, we can be sure that Paul discourages the people of Malta in the same manner as he did the people of Lystra. Acts 14:14-18

What do you think the snake represents?

_____

What does Paul's escape proclaim?

_____

I believe that the snake and its venom represent the sting of sin. There is no escape from the consequences of sin. It causes death. Christ, however, has conquered sin and death. As we enter into Jesus through baptism, our Savior removes the painful stinger. He gives us miraculous new life.

Write I Corinthians 15:55-57.

_____

_____

_____

Stop right now and say thank you to Jesus.

Luke does give us a brief account of some other happenings on the island.

✔ Read Acts 28:7-10.

Who is the chief official of the island? What is wrong with his father?

_____

What does Paul do? What is the result?

_____

_____

Publius, the first man of Malta, entertains the guests for three days in his home. This probably means he hosted the centurion, his leading officers, and Paul and his companions. As a result of his stay with Publius, Paul learns of his sick father. We notice here Dr. Luke's observations of the symptoms. Publius' father is suffering from dysentery — an intestinal infection that causes fever and severe bloody diarrhea. Paul goes in to see him, prays, lays his hands on the man, and heals him.

Word of the healing spreads quickly through the island and soon everyone is bringing their sick for Paul to heal. This, through the power of the Holy Spirit, Paul does. Once again, while Luke does not specifically tell us, we cannot imagine that Paul is silent about Christ. While we are not told of the harvest of souls Paul reaps on the island of Malta, we have no doubt that some of those people are now at the side of Jesus because of Paul's words.

● Read I Peter 2:24. How has Jesus healed you?

_____

_____

> We cannot overemphasize the power and sufficiency of the work of Jesus in our lives. In every thing and in every way He is the answer to our struggles. We must never become callused to the love and grace that saves us. Each day we must look in wonder at the blood of Jesus and fall on our knees, our hearts overflowing with gratitude and adoration.

# DAY 4

Paul is on his way to Rome. After surviving a shipwreck, he has had the opportunity to share the grace of God with the people of Malta. As spring arrives, the company prepares to go to Rome.

✔ Read Acts 28:11-16.

*On the map located at the beginning of Lesson 7, mark the route taken by Paul.*

How long does Paul stay on the island of Malta?

_____

Who comes to meet Paul in Puteoli? How long does he stay?

_____

● Paul has always dreamed of going to Rome for God. Why does the manner in which Paul is going to Rome hold an important lesson for us?

_____

_____

When spring arrives on Malta, the centurion and his passengers are able to board an Alexandrian ship that wintered on the island. The ship makes brief stops at Syracuse and Rhegium as it heads toward Rome. Finally, after a 200-mile journey from Rhegium, Paul's ship pulls into the Bay of Naples and port of Puteoli. Puteoli was the main port in Italy for the trade of grain along the Mediterranean. After debarking at Puteoli, Paul and his companions meet some Christians in the city. They are invited to stay with the brothers for a week. Again we see the liberty with which the Roman centurion treats Paul. Who knows? Maybe by this time Julius is a Christian brother as well.

The seventy-five-mile journey from Puteoli to Rome must be made on foot along the famous Appian Way. Word has been sent ahead to Rome of Paul's arrival in Italy. When Paul reaches the Forum of Appius, forty-three miles from Rome, he is greeted by Christians who have traveled from Rome to meet him. Imagine walking forty-three miles to meet somebody! Ten miles later, at the town of Three Taverns, another group of Roman Christians greets Paul. Paul is very thankful to see the Christians from Rome. Though they have never met before, they are joyful to finally meet Paul. They have read his letter (the book of Romans), and have anticipated his coming for three years. Paul, perhaps, was worried that they would be ashamed of his chains, but these Christians do much to encourage him.

● What special burdens do ministers, elders, deacons, and teachers carry? What can we do to lighten their load?

_____

When they reach Rome, accommodations are made for Paul. He is allowed to live in a rented house rather than in a Roman prison. He is still, of course, under constant guard. He lives under house arrest. This means that he is shackled to a guard by means of a long, light chain attached to his arm. Every four to six hours a new soldier takes a rotation as Paul's guard. While this is very lenient, it is nonetheless a difficult way to live. Imagine being shackled to someone twenty-four hours a day. That person would observe you at all times. No moment could be yours in private.

Paul, however, uses the situation as an opportunity to preach the gospel.

● Paul could have reacted in many different ways to being imprisoned. Think about some of his options. What lesson do you learn from Paul's choice?

_____

_____

Read Philippians 1:12-14. What is the result of Paul's imprisonment?

_____

● How do we live above our circumstances?

_____

_____

After Paul gets settled in his new surroundings, he begins to spread the message of the grace of God.

 Read Acts 28:17-28.

What is the first thing Paul does in Rome? What is the result of those first meetings?

_____

_____

As is his custom, Paul approaches the Jews in Rome first. He carefully explains the circumstances of his arrest and that he has done nothing to warrant imprisonment. The Jews tell him that they have received no communication from Jerusalem regarding him. This seems very unusual considering the Sanhedrin's vehemence against Paul. Nevertheless, the Jews agree to give him an audience to discuss the "sect" they have heard so much about. A week later a large crowd gathers to listen to Paul. In his usual manner, Paul presents the facts of the Law and the Prophets in the light of Jesus the Messiah. Also as usual, the reaction of the crowd is divided — some believe, some do not.

Paul, upon once again hearing the murmurs of disbelief, quotes the prophet Isaiah. Jesus Himself also used this passage with regard to the Jews' lack of faith. Paul turns again to the fertile hearts of the Gentiles. For many years, Paul has dreamed of coming to Rome for Jesus. We can be sure that he never dreamed it would be in Roman chains. Yet, God is working in a powerful way. Satan meant to silence the servant of God, but Paul uses his chains as a tool of the gospel.

● Describe a negative situation you found yourself in that God turned around and used for good.

_____

_____

✔ Read Acts 28:30-31.

How long is Paul under house arrest? Describe Paul's activities during this time.

_____

_____

For two years Paul boldly proclaims the grace of God to all who will listen. We know from the letters he writes during this time that Paul is refreshed by the companionship of many friends — Luke of course, the faithful Timothy, Tychicus and, amazingly, John Mark. Many others visit the apostle, including a man named Epaphroditus from Philippi. He brings a special gift of support from the Philippian church for Paul.

Despite his chains, this is a productive time in the life of Paul. As we will see, he writes several letters during this time in prison. He also has great success in bringing people to the love of Jesus.

Whose household has the gospel reached? Philippians 4:22

_____

● Why doesn't Luke wait to see the outcome of Paul's trial before closing the book of Acts? What do you think is the most important thing Luke wanted Theophilus to see about Christianity?

_____

_____

The gospel had reached the household of Caesar himself!

As we close the book of Acts, I would like for you to consider the following observation.

> The Book of Acts ends with Paul "preaching the kingdom of God, and teaching those things which concern the Lord Jesus Christ, with all confidence." The record is not concluded. The Holy Spirit continues to work today. The acts of the Holy Spirit have not been finished even in our day... The work of the church has not yet been completed; it is a continuing story. What you and I have done in the power of the Holy Spirit will be included in that record .[2]

What is the Holy Spirit writing about your life?

_____

_____

_____

1 Bruce, p369
2 McGee, *Acts, Chapters 15-28,* p174-175

155

# Joyful Grace

While Paul is in Rome under house arrest, he is able to do much to advance the gospel of Christ. One of the things for which we can be most grateful is the letters that he writes during this imprisonment. Paul writes four letters while under arrest in Rome. All refer to his bonds and chains and are known today as the prison letters. In these letters we also see a more mature, confident Paul. In his previous letters, he spent much time defending his apostleship. In these letters, Paul focuses completely on relationships — between both Christ and the believer and Christian to Christian. This week we will look at these four letters written from Rome during this time of Paul's imprisonment. Today we know these letters as Philemon, Colossians, Ephesians, and Philippians.

## DAY 1

It had long been Paul's dream to go to Rome and proclaim the grace of God. We can be sure that he never expected to go in chains!

● In what way had Satan hoped to defeat Paul? Did he succeed? What lesson do you see for your own life?

_____

_____

**Philemon**

✔ Read the letter to Philemon.

Describe Philemon.

_____

Who is Onesimus? What did he do?

_____

What request does Paul make of Philemon?

_____

While Paul is in Rome, he comes in contact with a runaway slave named Onesimus. While we are not told the nature of Onesimus' crime, many commentators agree that Onesimus had stolen something from Philemon and then run away to the crowds of Rome.

Paul takes Onesimus in and teaches him about Jesus. Paul sees the value of each soul, whether an emperor or a runaway slave. Onesimus responds to the grace of God and is baptized. Being a Christian now, however, poses him with a moral dilemma. He has sinned against his master and must, as a servant of God, go back and face the crime he committed. The Roman punishment for a slave caught stealing and escaping is death. Paul steps in and writes a letter to Philemon, appealing to him as a brother in Christ. Paul begins the letter by greeting Philemon and his wife, Apphia. Philemon is a prominent member of the church at Colossae. In fact, the church meets in their home. Paul also addresses Archippus, who seems to be either an elder of the church or a minister working there. After complimenting Philemon, Paul explains the situation. He tells Philemon of the change in Onesimus. Once he was a useless slave, now he is useful as a brother in Christ. This is a play on Onesimus' name, which means "useful." He tells Philemon how valuable Onesimus is to him and asks Philemon to accept Onesimus back with the forgiveness of Jesus. Paul even offers to pay for any damage done by Onesimus.

● What do we learn about forgiveness from Paul's letter to Philemon?

_____

_____

Paul ends the letter confident of Philemon's good heart. He asks him to prepare a guestroom in anticipation of Paul's release from prison.

We do not know of the outcome of the meeting between Philemon and Onesimus. We can only assume that Paul's letter smoothed the way.

● What does Paul's contact with Onesimus and his actions on his behalf teach you about Paul? About God? What lesson do we need to apply to our own lives?

_____

_____

Despite the personal nature of this letter, Paul manages to relate the story of the gospel.

● Where do you see our salvation by Jesus illustrated in this letter?

_____

_____

Paul purposely parallels the story of Onesimus to that of Philemon's acceptance of Jesus. If Jesus has forgiven us, how can we refuse to forgive each other?

First, there is an offense that causes a separation. Just as Onesimus' actions separated him from the good will of Philemon, so our sin separates us from God. Next we see the understanding of punishment. Onesimus knows that if he goes back to Philemon, the penalty is death. In the same way, our sin before God demands death as the punishment. We then have a beautiful picture of mediation. Paul steps in on Onesimus' behalf. He asks Philemon to charge him with Onesimus' wrongdoing. He even offers to pay back anything that Onesimus owes him. In the same way, Jesus intercedes with the Father on our behalf. He accepted our sin as His own. He even went so far as to fully pay the debt that we owe. Now Onesimus can return to Philemon without fear. With this grace, Onesimus returns, not just as a slave, but as a brother in Christ.

> Because of the blood of Jesus, we can approach the Father without fear. Yet, not only does Jesus allow us to go to God, He presents us to Him as His children and co-heirs with Christ. The forgiveness of Jesus completely changes us and our status before God.

Even here, in this short letter, Paul beautifully presents the grace of God and is a bold reminder of the words of Jesus.

Write John 13:34.

_____

_____

● Read Matthew 5:9 in light of the letter to Philemon. How can you be a peacemaker?

_____

_____

## DAY 2

### Colossians

When Tychicus and Onesimus deliver the letter to Philemon, they also deliver a letter from Paul to the entire church at Colosse. Colosse is a city about 100 miles from Ephesus. The church at Colosse was established during the three years that Paul preached in Ephesus. One of the principle teachers in Colosse has come to Rome with disturbing news for Paul. The church at Colosse is beset with false teachers. These men are teaching that in order to come to God, you must know more than Christ Jesus. They claim there are other things you must do and know to be close to God. The letter Paul writes to the Colossians is in response to that false teaching. Today these false teachings still abound. Men have taken the simple truth of the gospel and have added barriers on the path toward God. Some claim you must go to a man to reach God. Others claim you must meditate, follow a man-made creed, or have a mystical experience. The beauty of God's truth is that each individual may come directly to Him through the blood of Jesus alone.

● Today what kinds of things do men insist you must know or do in order to see God?

_____

_____

The most beautiful principle that Paul explains in Colossians is the supremacy of Jesus. It is on this section that we will spend our time.

✔ Read Colossians 1:13-23.

● Where do we live because of Christ?

_____

Paul explains four areas over which Christ is supreme. What are they?

_____

_____

_____

● Since Christ is supreme in all these areas, what do we need to know in order to know God?

_____

Paul begins by contrasting where we were as sinners with where we are as Christians. The language is an absolutely vivid picture of our new life in Christ. We have been rescued from the dominion of darkness and brought into the Kingdom of the Son!

● In what way are light and darkness excellent illustrations of our lives before and after Jesus?

_____

_____

_____

Paul then describes four areas in which Christ is supreme. These four areas encompass all of life.

First, Paul explains that Christ is supreme over all creation. By creation, Paul is referring to more than just the trees and flowers, though He certainly reigns over all that. Paul is also referring to the wisdom, power, and authority of man. Jesus is the Creator of man. He was with God in the beginning and all things were made for Him and through Him. Nothing that is created is greater than its Creator.

● Why is knowing Christ as Creator important to you?

_____

Second, Christ is supreme in the church. Jesus was the first one resurrected from the dead, never to experience death again. This makes Him head of the church. The body is worthless without the head, dependent on it for existence and usefulness.

● What is your relationship to Christ in the church?

_____

Third, Christ is supreme in the redemption of man. Through His work on the cross, man is reconciled with God because of the blood of Jesus. It is through Him that we have peace with God. There is no other way.

● How have you answered Jesus' invitation of redemption?

_____

Finally, Christ is supreme in our personal lives. Because of our transformation from darkness to light, He presents us clean and holy to His Father. It is because of the blood of Jesus and our obedience to it that we can daily find forgiveness.

✔ Read Colossians 3:1-17. What practical changes does Christ's supremacy make in our personal lives? Of what kind of things are we to rid ourselves? What are we to add to our lives because of Christ? Which list is easier to do? Why?

_____

_____

_____

_____

Through explaining Christ's supremacy from the very broad — all of creation — to the very specific — our hearts, Paul shows us that knowing Jesus is all we need to draw near to God.

# DAY 3

Satan has tried to silence the apostle Paul by placing him in Roman chains. Arresting Paul, however, does little to quiet him. Beyond his constant teaching to those surrounding him, his pen flies over the paper as he writes letters to those he loves in the Lord. God uses Paul's time in prison to write the New Testament for us.

**Ephesians**

While delivering the letters to Philemon and Colosse, Tychius also delivers a letter to Paul's beloved friends in Ephesus. This letter is a letter of encouragement and instruction and is to be circulated among all the churches of the area.

Ephesians is an immensely practical letter. It is filled with pictures of the influence of mature Christians at home, in the church, and in the world.

One striking illustration concludes the letter to the Ephesians. It is a picture of the armor of God defending the Christian from the attacks of Satan. It is especially fitting to read this passage in light of Paul's being chained to a Roman guard twenty-four hours a day.

 Read Ephesians 6:10-18.

● In what ways are Christians attacked by the powers described in Ephesians 6:11-12?

_____

_____

Match the piece of armor with the spiritual protection it offers.

| | |
|---|---|
| Belt | Faith |
| Breastplate | Gospel of Peace |
| Feet | Righteousness |
| Helmet | Salvation |
| Shield | Truth |
| Sword | Word of God |

What additional weapon does the Christian have in Ephesians 6:18?

_____

Paul, perhaps better than anyone, understands that we are involved in a spiritual battle. His physical captor may be the Romans, but the real enemy is Satan. Satan hates God and will do anything to make His children fall. In response to this attack, we are to prepare ourselves by putting on the full armor of God. Notice that Paul does not say that we must defeat Satan. Jesus has already done that. Instead we are to stand firm during the attack. Paul uses the soldier standing before him as a model of the spiritual armor we are to put on.

First, we are to put on the belt of truth. Truth is always the first defense against Satan. We are to encircle ourselves with it, surround ourselves with the truth.

● Why is truth the first of our weapons against Satan?

_____

Next comes the breastplate of righteousness. The righteousness of Jesus is to cover our hearts. We are to maintain our purity and holiness in our Christian walk. If we keep our hearts covered with this righteousness, the enemy has no advantage.

● How does righteousness blunt Satan's attacks?

_____

Third, our feet are to be protected by the gospel of peace. Wherever we go and whatever we do, we are to take the message of peace with us.

● What kind of peace do we have? Philippians 4:7

_____

Fourth, we are to pick up the shield of faith. Paul is looking at a soldier holding an oblong, leather-covered shield. When attacked by flaming arrows, the soldier could dip the shield in water and the arrows would do no harm. Likewise, our faith is our shield. When Satan attacks, he plants doubt and mistrust. Our faith, immersed in the Living Water, allows us to quench his arrows. We may not have all the answers, but we have faith in the One who does.

● Define faith. II Timothy 1:12

_____

Salvation is pictured as a helmet. Salvation begins with understanding and not emotion. Our knowledge of Jesus as our Savior will give us victory.

Why is chasing after a spiritual feeling or emotion dangerous?

_____

Finally, we are to hold the sword of the Spirit, which is the word of God. By knowing the word of God, we can repel Satan's attacks. He uses our lack of understanding to draw us into sin. By studying the Bible, we arm ourselves against the attacks of Satan.

● How does Satan seek to exploit our lack of spiritual knowledge?

_____

_____

The last weapon Paul describes is the weapon of prayer. Through prayer, we enter the throne room of God and seek His protection and guidance. Paul tells us here not to try to fight the enemy alone. When Satan is assaulting you, go to your Heavenly Father in prayer.

● How often do you use the weapon of prayer?

_____

There are two important points before we leave this powerful picture.

First, a firefighter does not wait until he is in the burning house to put on his fireproof suit. He prepares before he goes into the burning house. In a similar way, we must prepare for Satan before he starts launching flaming arrows at us. Surrounding ourselves daily with truth, righteousness, peace, and God's word are essential if we are to stand firm in Christ.

Secondly, I want you to see something vital.

Who is Truth?  _____  John 14:6

Who is our Righteousness? _____  I Corinthians 1:30

Who is our Peace?  _____  Ephesians 2:14

In whom do we have Faith?  _____  Romans 3:22

From whom do we receive Salvation? _____  I Thessalonians 5:9

Who is the Word of God? _____  John 1:1

In whose name do we pray?  _____  John 14:13-14

We must put on Jesus Christ. Only by surrounding ourselves in Him can we hope to survive the attacks of Satan. In Him is our protection and our salvation.

Write Galatians 3:26-27.

_____

_____

_____

● Picture yourself in the armor of God. Which of these tools do you use most frequently? Which do you use the least?

_____

_____

How do we daily put on the armor of God?

_____

_____

# DAY 4

**Philippians**

Some months pass before Paul writes another letter from his Roman imprisonment. The occasion for writing this letter is the visit from Philippi by Epaphroditus. He brings a substantial gift from the Philippian church to aid Paul while he is in prison. While in Rome, Epaphroditus becomes quite ill and Paul writes of his tremendous grief over the illness. When Epaphroditus recovers enough to return to Philippi, he takes this letter from Paul with him.

The letter to the church in Philippi has a different tone than the previous three. Paul appears to be under considerable stress. At this point, he has been in prison for four years, two years in Caesarea and two in Rome. Exhausted and humiliated, he must now be worried that this is how he will spend the rest of his life. The political situation in Rome is worsening with Nero as Emperor, and Paul is concerned about obtaining a positive outcome for his case.

Amidst all this pressure, Paul focuses on Jesus. He reassures the faithful Philippians that he is fine and thanks them for their generous gift.

 Remembering that Paul is chained to a guard as he writes, read Philippians 4:4-13.

What four heart attitudes does Paul discuss in this passage?

_____

_____

● How are these four things possible in times of great stress?

_____

_____

● How do you acquire these four attitudes?

_____

_____

● How might Philippians 2:5-11 be the key to the four attitudes of the heart described by Paul?

_____

_____

This is a remarkable passage, made even more so by the fact that Paul had been in prison for the last four years. In this letter, he outlines four attitudes that are key to the Christian heart.

*The first is joy.* Joy is not controlled by circumstances. Joy allows circumstances, whatever they may be, to be used for Jesus. Joy is not about things. It is about priorities.

Read Philippians 3:10-11. What is Paul's priority?

_____

When our focus is Jesus, we see the hand of God everywhere we turn. We see Him in the people that we meet, we hear His voice as the wind blows, and we feel His hand in the hugs of our children. That is joy.

*The second is gentleness.* Gentleness is quiet strength. No one likes to be bullied. The heart responds to one who is willing to take time and energy to share God. Intimately tied to gentleness is love and patience. They are bound up together.

Gentleness is not a priority in our society. This is precisely the reason it is a shining indication of God's presence in our lives. While Paul never allows evil to walk over him, he always has time and patience for those seeking God.

● How do you define gentleness. Read I Peter 3:3-4. Why is a gentle spirit so precious to God?

_____

_____

*The third heart attitude Paul displays is peace.* Peace defies the world's logic. You can't find a person on the street that is not "anxious" or "stressed" today. Our society almost wears it as a badge of pride. Satan wants us to be "stressed out." It takes a lot of energy and time. If we use that energy to focus on our anxiety then we lessen our ability to focus on God.

Peace comes into our hearts by laying all of our anxieties and stresses at the feet of Jesus. When we acknowledge our dependence on Him, He gives us peace.

*Finally, and perhaps most rare, Paul shows us the attitude of contentment.* Paul has lived in every kind of circumstance. He has lived in luxury and he has sat in a filthy, stinky dungeon. More importantly, Paul knows the emptiness of a heart without Jesus and the fullness of serving Jesus. He knows that the gift he holds dear in his heart — the presence of his Lord — is more important than what kind of house he lives in, what kind of clothes he wears, or what kind of food he eats.

Write Philippians 3:8.

_____

_____

_____

What do you think Paul had given up? We know he gave up wealth, family, power, security, position, and roots to live a life of wandering, dependent on the charity of others, ridiculed, imprisoned, and in physical danger. It is all worth it, Paul tells us, just to know Jesus. All of the luxuries in the world mean nothing without the richness of Christ.

● What benefits does being in Christ bring to your life?

_____

_____

Read your list the next time you are called to sacrifice for the Lord.

It is important to note that these four heart attitudes have to be learned. It takes effort to incorporate them in your life. Rejoicing is a verb, not an adjective. Gentleness requires practiced restraint. Peace comes from active prayer. Contentment is learned through committed focus. These four attitudes are the treasures of a disciplined, Christ-focused heart.

● In very practical terms, how do we learn to rejoice, be gentle, have peace, and be content?

_____

_____

Are you stressed out? Is your heart full of anxiety? Have you been robbed of your joy? Turn to Jesus. Focus on Him. Make Him your priority. Take time to learn.

# Victorious Grace

We have come to the end of the life of Paul. I have grown to love Paul through the writing of this material and I pray you have come to love him as well. We have watched as Jesus reached out and changed the heart of Paul as a young man. Molding him through the influence of Ananias and Barnabas, God prepared Paul to take the message of Jesus throughout the Gentile world. We walked with Paul as he went from city to city preaching the grace of God. We winced as he was beaten, listened as he sang in prison, watched as the hatred of the Jews grew and tormented him. We heard him proclaim with courage the gospel to rulers and kings. We held our breath as the boat that took him to Rome sank in the sea. We have read the letters he wrote while chained to a Roman guard. No one has lived a greater life of service for our Lord than Paul.

## DAY 1

The last years of the life of Paul must be pieced together from bits of information we gather from his last three letters and secular historical records.

"It was universally believed that St. Paul's appeal to Caesar terminated successfully; that he was acquitted of the charges laid against him; and that he spent some years of freedom before he was again imprisoned and condemned."[1]

Though we know nothing of Paul's trial before Caesar, we do know that he regained his freedom sometime in the spring of 63 AD. God assured Paul that he would testify His name before Caesar, so we can only assume that Paul had his day in court before Nero. After hearing the charges against Paul and the witnesses produced by the Sanhedrin in Jerusalem, Paul is released.

What Paul did during the next four to five years can only be gleaned from references to cities he visited mentioned in his letters to Timothy and Titus.

Look at the following references and note the cities to which Paul refers.

I Timothy 1:3 _____

Titus 1:5 _____

II Timothy 4:20 _____

Titus 3:12 _____

From the list above, it appears that Paul revisits many of the churches he loves so dearly. He apparently goes to Ephesus, Philippi in Macedonia, Crete, Corinth, Miletus, and Nicopolis. The secular historical record is quite convincing that Paul also spent time in Spain after his release from prison. There is, however, no Scriptural record of that visit beyond his desire to visit Spain expressed in Romans 15:24. There is no way to ascertain the path that Paul followed as he visits these towns filled with Christians he loves so dearly.

Paul leaves Timothy in Ephesus to continue the work of strengthening the church. Timothy has been a faithful companion of Paul for many years. He joined Paul in his mission work at the beginning of the second missionary journey.

How does Paul describe Timothy in I Timothy 1:2?

_____

Paul seems to have written his first letter to Timothy from Philippi in Macedonia. The important characteristic of this letter, as well as his letter to Titus, is the preparation of these two young men to take over leadership of the church. Paul knew he would not live forever. He knew the future of the church was going to rest, in part, in the hands of Timothy and Titus.

> Part of our responsibilities as mature Christians is to train the next generation to continue the work.

● How can we help train others to lead the body of Christ?

_____

_____

The training and selection of godly leaders is very important and Paul spends much time with Timothy and Titus explaining qualifications of those chosen to be elders and deacons.

In fact, why was Titus left in Crete? Titus 1:5

_____

Read I Timothy 3:1-7 and Titus 1:6-9. Make a list of the qualifications of an elder.

_____

_____

_____

This is not a list only for men wishing to be elders. This is a checklist for all Christians. These should be our goals as we strive for Christian maturity.

● Look at the list. Honestly evaluate your own heart in its light. Which of these areas of maturity and service do you most need to work on in your Christian walk? Which one do you most want to work on in the next six months?

_____

_____

Ask God to help you grow where you are deficient.

● How does a wife help her husband become like the man described in I Timothy 3 and Titus 1?

_____

_____

# DAY 2

We have been talking about training people for the Lord. Paul spent a great deal of time training Timothy and Titus when they were very young men. Our society, and even the church I fear, has extremely low expectations of our teenagers. We assume they are frivolous, inattentive, uncaring, and incapable of self-discipline. That is Satan talking. Our young people have remarkable potential for God. They certainly need guidance and training, and while they will make mistakes, God wants to use our children in a powerful way. We should not underestimate their heart for Jesus.

 Read I Timothy 4:12.

To whom can young people set an example?

_____

● In what areas of Christian life can a young person set a positive example?

_____

_____

Our young people can be an example for all of us. They have tremendous potential for faith, generosity, and love. Paul tells Timothy that he can be an example to all believers in the areas of speech, life, love, faith, and purity. That just about covers the whole Christian walk, except public leadership in the church. I challenge you to raise the bar of expectations for your teenagers. Don't sell them short. If you do, you not only rob them of a blessing, you rob yourself as well.

By the way, training for a Christian walk like this doesn't start at fourteen years old.

Read II Timothy 1:5 and 3:15. When did Timothy receive his first training for Christ?

_____

That's right. When he was being held in the arms of his mother and grandmother. God has put that responsibility squarely in your lap, so to speak.

● How do you train your children to be a godly example like Timothy?

_____

_____

After a period of about four years, we are able to pick up Paul's whereabouts. In the middle of winter, in 67 AD, Paul is at Troas.

✔ Read II Timothy 4:13.

At whose house is Paul staying? What does he leave behind?

_____

_____

In 64 AD, Nero burns Rome. In order to deny suspicion that he torched Rome, Nero accuses the Christians of lighting the match. This begins a terrible persecution of Christians throughout the Roman Empire.

Evidently, as Paul is staying in the home of Carpus at Troas, the Romans arrest him. So swift is the arrest that Paul does not even have time to retrieve his cloak and precious papers. He is taken immediately to Rome to stand trial.

His second Roman imprisonment is not nearly as lenient as his first. Instead of a rented house, Paul is forced into the Mamertime dungeon where he is chained like a criminal.

The second letter to Timothy is written from this dungeon. It is both a sad and victorious letter. It is sad because of Paul's obvious suffering. Here deprived of friendship and alone, he can see with certainty that his life is almost over. Yet, in this fact, there is also victory. Paul looks forward to seeing the face of Jesus.

Read the following and note how Paul is treated in the Mamertime prison.

II Timothy 1:8 _____

II Timothy 1:15 _____

II Timothy 1:17 _____

II Timothy 2:9 _____

II Timothy 4:10-16 _____

*172*

● What change in tone do you detect in Paul's letters written during this time in contrast to his earlier letters?

_____

● What is the most difficult burden for Paul at the end of his life? How have you dealt with this burden in your own life?

_____

_____

This is a difficult time for Paul. Deserted by everyone except Luke, the loneliness and isolation are oppressive. Chained, he is being treated like a common criminal. Friends who do try to find him have a difficult time. The persecution becomes so fierce that it is dangerous to be seen with Paul.

# DAY 3

Despite the difficulties of being imprisoned, Paul seeks to encourage Timothy. He reminds him of his commitment to the gospel of Christ and gives him important instructions regarding the work ahead.

✔ Read Acts 20:24 and I Corinthians 9:24-25.

● In what way is the Christian life like a race?

_____

● What is the most important part of a race?

_____

What advice does the writer of Hebrews give us on how to successfully run the race? Hebrews 12:1-3

_____

_____

The writer of Hebrews offers us five training tips that will help us run a successful Christian race.

Training Tip #1: **Listen to your cheering section.** You are not running the race alone. Many faithful people have already crossed the finish line. Their example can encourage and strengthen us. The Holy Spirit is our constant running companion. Fellow Christians can cheer us on, help us up when we fall, and motivate us to keep up the pace. And, if you listen carefully, you will hear applause coming from nail-scarred hands.

● How can others help you in your Christian race?

_____

_____

Training tip #2: **Run with perseverance.** The Christian life is a long-distance marathon, not a sprint. It is characterized more by a consistent, regular pace than the occasional bursts of speed.

● How do you build endurance for the race?

_____

_____

Training tip #3: **Let go of baggage that slows you down.** Our coach here in Hebrews tells us to throw off everything that hinders or entangles us. We must not carry the loads of sin, guilt, and fear on our run. They will weigh us down and make our feet so heavy we won't be able to take the next step. Jesus has carried those things for us so that we don't have to.

● What baggage is slowing you down?

_____

_____

Training Tip #4: **Stay on the marked course.** We are not pioneering an unmarked trail. We are to run on the path marked for us by Jesus Christ. He is the trailblazer. He has already gone where we need to go. A runner who veers off the path will expend extra energy, encounter hazardous hurdles, and have a hard time finding the finish line.

● What trail markers has Jesus left for you to follow?

_____

_____

Training tip #5: **Fix our eyes on the prize winner.** Most important to the successful running of the race is keeping our focus on the finish line. Keeping our goal in mind will help us endure the steep hills, overcome leg cramps, give us joy on the downhill slopes, and keep us on the path. We need to fix our eyes on Jesus. He has run the race, endured the wall of pain, broken the finishing tape, and now stands victorious on the winner's block.

● How do you keep your focus on Jesus?

_____

_____

Where in the race are you now?

| | |
|---|---|
| _____ Haven't even started | _____ Moved to the sidelines |
| _____ Just out of the starting blocks | _____ In the long stretch |
| _____ Having leg cramps | _____ Close to completing the race |

> Have confidence that when you reach the finish line you'll find Jesus standing there, arms open wide, joyously waiting to place the crown of victory on your head.

## DAY 4

As we say goodbye to Paul, let's close with these final words.

Write II Timothy 4:6-8.

_____

_____

_____

● What would you like to be able to say about your life at the end of your life? What are you doing today to make that a reality?

_____

_____

_____

Tradition holds that Paul was executed during the last year of the reign of Nero. He was taken outside the city about three miles on the Ostian Road. There the executioner swings the ax and beheads Paul. As Paul enters the gates of Paradise, we can be sure that the Master welcomes him with these words, *"Well done, good and faithful servant!"* Matthew 25:21

Paul dies as he had lived, filled with love for Jesus.

● What is the most important lesson you have learned from the life of Paul? What is the most important thing you have learned about God?

_____

_____

It has been said that after the resurrection, the greatest testimony to the truth and validity of Christianity is the changed life of the apostle Paul. No one speaks more eloquently about the impact of the grace of God and its power to change the heart of man than Paul.

We have watched Saul as he murderously persecuted and pursued those who claimed the name of Christ. We witnessed this man literally and spiritually fall to the ground when surrounded by the light of grace. We held our breath in wonder as we watched Jesus extend His love and embrace the one who had defiled His Name.

We have walked with Paul from city to city and looked into the eyes of soul after soul as he preached the life-changing message of the gospel. We have watched him work miracles in Jesus' name and hang his head in disappointment at the hard-hearted Jews. We swam with him as his ship sank and have been infused with courage by his boldness.

Nothing inspires us more, however, than his passion and his focus. Paul daily *"resolved to know nothing…except Jesus Christ and him crucified."* (I Corinthians 2:2) and he challenges us to do the same.

The life of Paul motivates us to think beyond the limits of our own imaginations and see the potential of one Christian determined to walk in the footsteps of Jesus. He inspires us to commit ourselves to Christ, to make our lives full expressions of His love, and to stand with courage for His name. A Christian with that kind focus and passion, God can use to change the world.

The most miraculous part of Paul's story is not about Paul at all. The best part is that the power of God's grace is available to you today. God wasn't just looking for Paul on the road to Damascus —He was looking for a heart that would long to be like Him, that would burn to share His love, that would rest in His forgiveness.

He is still looking for that kind of heart today. Hearts willing to walk — by the grace of God.

_____

1 Conybeare, p738

# Bibliography

Bruce, F.F. *Paul: Apostle of the Heart Set Free*. Paternoster Press, Ltd., 1977.

Coffman, James Burton. *Acts*. Abilene: ACU Press, 1977.

Coffman, James Burton. *I & II Corinthians*. Abilene: ACU Press, 1977.

Coffman, James Burton. *Galatians, Ephesians, Philippians & Colossians*. Abilene: ACU Press, 1977.

Conybeare & Howson. *The Life & Epistles of St. Paul*. Grand Rapids: Wm. B. Eerdmans Publishing Co., reprinted 1968.

Davis, John D. *Davis Dictionary of the Bible*. Nashville: Royal Publishing, Inc., 1973.

Gutherie, Donald. *The Apostles*. Grand Rapids: Zondervan, 1975.

*Life Application Bible*. Grand Rapids: Tyndale House Publishers, Inc./Zondervan Publishing House, 1991.

McGee, J. Vernon. *Acts, Chapters 1-14*. Nashville: Thomas Nelson Publishers, 1991.

McGee, J. Vernon. *Acts, Chapters 15-28*. Nashville: Thomas Nelson Publishers, 1991.

Meyer, F.B. *Great Men of the Bible, Volume II*. Grand Rapids: Zondervan, 1982.

*The NIV Serendipity Bible For Study Groups*. Grand Rapids: Zondervan Publishing House, 1989.

*The NIV Study Bible*. Grand Rapids: Zondervan, 1985.

Shepherd, J.W. *The Church, The Falling Away, and The Restoration*. Nashville: Gospel Advocate Co., 1929.

Tenney, Merrill, C. *New Testament Survey*. Grand Rapids: Wm. B. Eerdmans Publishing Co., 1961.

Zodhiates, Spiros, Th.D. *The Hebrew-Greek Key Study Bible*. Chattanooga: AMG Publishers, 1990.

# Meet Casandra Martin, author of the popular Women Opening the Word Bible study series.

**Casandra Martin**
(Photographer: Eubanks Photography)

At home in Spring, Texas, Casandra Martin loves teaching women. "I have a passion for teaching women about Jesus. There is something so special about women coming together to learn from God's Word."

Casandra graduated from Harding University, where she met and married her husband, Ken. After college, Casandra taught at Northland Christian School where she was named Teacher of the Year. Following several years of teaching high school, God gave Casandra her greatest teaching assignment – her children, Emily, Ryan, and Jonathan.

As a stay-at-home mom, God opened the door for Casandra to use her teaching skills to teach women about God's Word and His love for them. Her experience in working with women in the church includes teaching and coordinating ladies' Bible classes as well as serving as the Spiritual Growth Coordinator for a Women's Ministry Steering Committee. Casandra also enjoys sharing with many of God's women while speaking at retreats, ladies' days, and Bible lectureships.

Casandra and her family worship and work with God's people at the church of Christ in Champions.

---

# Books in the Series, Women Opening the Word (WOW)

Echoing His Heartbeat: The Life of David

God Pass By Me: Seeing God's Glory through His Names, Titles, and Descriptions

A Light in the Darkness: Elijah and Elisha

Paul: by the Grace of God

The Shadow of the Cross